A LUCKY NUMBER

A Lucky Number

BY

VERA HENRY

WITH DRAWINGS BY

VASILIU

J. B. Lippincott Company
Philadelphia and New York

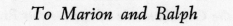
To Marion and Ralph

If anyone should ask, there is a town on the Canadian side of the Detroit River, much like this, but not exactly. The people who lived there resembled the characters in this book, but not entirely, and in so far as I know, none of them bore the names used here. But are the stories true? Well, yes—and no.

·CONTENTS·

A LUCKY NUMBER

·ONE·

The Temptress

There's no getting away from the fact that my mother liked men. She frankly and completely believed they were the most magnificent, fascinating creatures on God's good earth. They could unstick drawers and open stubborn jars and balance bank accounts. Under the shining approval in her blue eyes every male stood a little taller than he really was. All this might have led to complications except for one obvious fact.

All men had their splendor, but it was most apparent Mother believed that Father was the king of them all.

In fact her trouble with the laundryman would never have begun in the first place if she had stuck to Yardley's English Lavender perfume.

For years that clean, cool smell was a part of the house. There were dried-leaf sachets among the sheets and in the bureau drawers, and when she went out Mother always sprinkled a few drops of toilet water on her hanky and the front of her dress.

I remember one time my sister Bonnie fell in love with, of all people, Tom Grecy (Tom looked distinguished, but actually it was just a good, healthy head of hair). We girls couldn't understand it. Then one night Bonnie woke me up. She looked white and shaken.

"I've made such an awful mistake," she wailed. "It wasn't Tom I liked. It was that lavender shaving lotion he uses. He smells just like Mother!"

All of us girls were very relieved thinking we were rid of Tom Grecy but he kept right on coming to the house to see Mother. All of our ex-boy friends did. It was downright embarrassing sometimes, to come home with a new date and find three or four of his predecessors out in the kitchen eating chess tarts and telling their troubles to Mother.

When it came to attracting men, Mother could have taught Cleopatra a thing or two. Mother in a size-42 print dress and black oxfords, with no more make-up than a bit of talcum rubbed on with a chamois, could come into a room and every man there straightened his tie and made straight for her.

This never bothered Father in the slightest. It simply confirmed his own good judgment.

For years Mother went comfortably through life getting seats on crowded buses or the finest steak from the butcher with a nice bit of suet thrown in, and then something happened.

My sister Bonnie gave Mother one of those perfume-testing sets for her birthday. It was a little crystal box filled with about a hundred tiny tubes of different kinds of perfume with wonderful names like My Sin and Breathless and Perhaps. (Actually, Bonnie had an ulterior motive in giving the set to Mother. She thought she would be able to borrow it back.) Mother however was as delighted as a child with a new toy.

"Why would anyone want to smell a hundred different ways?" she wondered.

"You don't," Bonnie explained. "You try to find the perfume that expresses your personality."

Mother was so pleased with the whole idea, she couldn't wait for one perfume to wear off before she started trying a new one.

"Angus, dear," she said to Father, "do you think my right or my left arm smells better?"

Father, who did most of his bookkeeping at home, looked up from his roll-top desk bewildered. "Is there a difference?"

"Of course, dear," said Mother. "My left arm is an Oriental Blend and the right is a Single Floral fragrance."

Father looked baffled. "How do you know?"

"Because it says so on the bottle. I had no idea that choosing a perfume was so complicated. I'm definitely not the Woodsy-Mossy type. I like the Spicy, but it doesn't like me—evaporates right off my skin. So far I seem to be the Fruity Blend. Would you have said I was the Fruity Blend?"

"I've never really given it the proper amount of thought," Father admitted.

"The Modern Blend might be better," she said. "But it seems so sophisticated. Smell again, dear."

He took a deep sniff. "They all smell the same to me."

"You've blunted your nose," Mother sighed. "If you smell too many kinds too close together you blunt your nose."

"Personally," said Father, "I like people to smell like people."

Even Father's lack of co-operation didn't stop Mother. She just went on trying out new types of perfume. The place took on a strange, hothouse smell. Pumpernickel, our dog, looked as if he were on the verge of a nervous breakdown. Father went around muttering that he felt as if he was living in sin with a different woman in his room every night.

Then something terrible happened.

Mr. Mendleson, the laundryman, tried to kiss Mother. Mr. Mendleson was a quiet little man with strong white teeth like oblongs of laundry soap. He had never acted like this before and Mother was very upset.

"I can't imagine for the life of me what came over him," she declared. "You know how pleasant and prompt he's always been about deliveries and replacing that old muslin sheet with a nice percale when it was lost."

"Calm down, dear," we said. "Now just what happened?"

Mother wrung her hands. "He put the laundry on the dining-room table, just the same as usual. I remember I said something about how easily he carried that heavy bundle. I opened my purse to pay him, and didn't have the right change, so I got it out of the teapot. Then I noticed he was breathing sort of funny and I asked if he was having trouble with his asthma again. Next thing I knew, he—he tried to put his arms around me. I was that surprised you could have knocked me over with a feather. I got away and ran outside—I can't imagine what the neighbors thought—me being chased around the petunia bed by the laundryman. I was never so mortified in my whole life."

Father reached grimly for his hat (the one Mother said made him look like a bank manager). "I," he said, "am going to have a little talk with Mr. Mendleson."

Mother tried to stop him, but Father was a stubborn man.

After he was gone, she was almost frantic. "Your father just doesn't realize his own strength," she kept saying. "Suppose he hurts that poor little fellow."

There was a dreadful silence while we pictured lurid headlines that said, "PROMINENT BUSINESSMAN SLAYS LAUNDRY DRIVER."

Bonnie began to cry. "Poor Daddy," she wept. "Poor Daddy. We must all stand by him."

"I wonder," said Senna, "If people really do bake saws in cakes."

Every time the phone rang we all rushed for it, but it was only boys trying to make dates.

About five-thirty Father came home. He gave Mother a kiss that skidded off the side of her cheek. "Sorry I'm late," he said. "What's for dinner?"

"How about Mr. Mendleson?" we all demanded. "Didn't you see him?"

"Mendleson?" said Father vaguely. "Oh, him—As a matter of fact, I did."

"What happened?" we asked. "What did he say?"

Father took a long time to light his pipe. "Flora," he said to Mother, "you're sure that maybe without meaning to—you didn't lead him on a little?"

"Lead him on! Lead him on!" Mother's blue eyes filled with outraged tears. "Angus, how can you say such a thing! You know perfectly well, all the years we've been married, I've never as much as looked at another man!"

Now this was quite true. It was the men who looked at Mother, though up until now, only with wistful respect.

"He was willing to come over to apologize but I thought it wasn't necessary," Father said. "As a matter of fact, I felt sorry for him."

"Sorry for him!" cried Mother. "Sorry!"

"He said he couldn't help himself," Father went on. "And in a way, I don't blame him. I know how it is. I, myself—"

He stopped at a warning cough from Mother.

We girls looked at her thoughtfully. She had brought us up to be polite, healthy and well behaved, but had she told us All?

"He said he looked at your blue eyes," Father told her, "and then he smelled perfume and he seemed to completely lose control of himself."

"The perfume!" we cried. "That was it! All it took was Mother plus perfume to push him over the border."

Mother sat down heavily. In her mind I think she was remembering those perfume ads with lovely scented ladies pursued by smoldering-eyed young men.

"But it wouldn't have the same result on an old lady like me," she protested.

We'd seen Mother in action without perfume.

"All I hope," said Senna, "is that when I'm Mother's age, some man will want to chase me around a petunia bed."

"What perfume were you using, Mother?" we demanded eagerly.

If it worked for Mother, by some lovely miracle it might work for her daughters too.

We never knew. Mother had simply opened a little bottle, used it and thrown it away. It might have been Passion or True Love or Forever Yours or any other of the hundred brands. The secret was lost forever.

Mother was so provoked at Father for doubting her that she gave him the smallest piece of raisin pie for dessert.

Before he went to bed that night, Father fixed the pulley on the clothesline, the bathroom faucet that had been leaking for a month, and put up a new shelf in the broom closet.

Although it was a weekday, Mother made popovers next morning in the iron gem pans that our great-grandmother had brought over from Scotland.

As for Mr. Mendleson, he gave up his route and retired to a chicken farm where he did very well. We had a new laundryman who was quite prompt with deliveries and good about replacing things that got lost.

Just to be on the safe side, Mother went back to using Yardley's Lavender.

·TWO·

A Matter of Duty

Every time the stork flapped his wings in the vicinity of our house, Mother began knitting little pale blue sweaters and socks. In due course the doctor would poke his head out the bedroom door and say, "It's another girl!"

My father would always rise gallantly to the occasion and say that was exactly what he had wanted all the time, but Mother never did learn. She just went on sewing little blue ribbons onto the next batch of baby clothes.

Since the name selected for the expected baby had, of course, been a boy's name, when it came time for christening, there was nothing to do but toss an "a" on the end and hope for the best. That is how it happened that my sisters and I are listed in the Essex County records as Victoria, Thomasina, Roberta, Leslie and Donalda. These names in turn became corrupted to Vicki—that's me—Senna, Bonnie, and the twins, Lee and Duff.

Our multiple identity always caused some confusion in the town and this, together with the fact that the house was continually bursting at the seams with assorted cousins and neighborhood kids, made an accurate statistical count rather difficult. There are neighbors of ours who even yet will tell you that there were at least twenty-two Tippett girls. This, of course, is a complete exaggeration. There were only five.

We grew up in a huge old brick house on the Canadian side of the river, facing Detroit. The house itself was a soft cream and bright-flowered trumpet vines and ivy clung to its walls. For all its respectable air it had had quite a past. At one time it had belonged to a rumrunner and swift, silent-motored boats had slid out into the darkness of the Detroit River from the very dock where the younger children used to play with their dolls. Indeed, for years we always hoped to find a secret room or passage within the house, but we never did.

After the rumrunner ran into a little penitentiary trouble, the place changed hands rapidly or stood empty, for it was too large for most people. Father bought it for a very reasonable sum and Mother furnished it with a placid mingling of Eaton's catalogue and heirloom antiques.

The six bedrooms were always full, though only in the last few years did the beds boast innerspring mattresses. This was because Father could sleep peacefully on a gravel road and our energetic little mother was convinced that sleeping was nothing but a bad habit. She herself would prowl around all night, covering her offspring and rubbing warm goose grease on the chest of anyone who coughed, or even breathed as if she might be considering having a cough next week.

At six next morning, Mother was up, and busy as a

robin. After patiently waiting until six-thirty, with an air of the day being practically over, she would make the rounds of the bedrooms.

"Girls," she would call, "Girls, I don't see how you can bear to waste this lovely morning just lying in bed"—this even if it happened to be pouring rain and we had been to a dance the night before. Eventually, after hearing this announcement made at fifteen-minute intervals, we got up in self-defense. When my sister Bonnie announced her engagement, we all looked at her in envy. "Gosh," we said. "When you're married, you'll be able to sleep in mornings."

While the house on the river had some unusual aspects, we were an average Canadian family. We warmed the pot before making tea, called the last letter of the alphabet "zed," and considered anyone who didn't know the capital of Alberta rather poorly educated.

Our mother in particular had been brought up carefully. She was a small-town girl who had married at eighteen, wearing a dress of shadow lace with a hand-span waistline. She belonged to the Daughters of the Empire, the Women's Institute and the Philathea Bible Class. She lived a gently virtuous life, with one exception.

She was an accomplished smuggler.

She was a law-abiding citizen by nature and the sort of woman who would not lie, even about her age. She became enmeshed in circumstances beyond her control when we moved from Toronto to the house on the border.

There was a splendid view of the American skyline from

our living-room window and it soon became so familiar it was difficult to realize that it was actually in foreign territory. Then too, it may be that some spirit of lawlessness still lingered in the air from the days when our house had belonged to a rumrunner. At any rate, it was so harmless an errand as buying kitchen curtains for her new home that led to Mother's downfall.

She took the inter-urban street car into town to go shopping—a little indignant at having to pay a double fare because we lived so far out, but she could not find just the sort of yellow ruffled curtain that she had in mind in all Windsor.

She looked across the pen-point narrowness of the river towards Detroit and it occurred to her that in addition to its magnificent skyscrapers, it must also have stores.

Now Detroit might be only a scant five-minute ferry ride away, but in spirit it might as well have been on the other side of the world. My mother's people had been United Empire Loyalists and even yet she was indignant every time she thought of the War of 1812. Moreover, this was during Prohibition days, when the goings on in Detroit, as reported by the Sunday supplements, were enough to frizzle your hair.

The curtains, however, were necessary for Mother's social life, since, in a new neighborhood, their absence meant she was not yet willing to receive callers.

After some troubled consideration Mother deposited her nickel and walked through the gate and onto the ferry. It was a pleasant ride that almost soothed her fears. When she got off the boat an American Immigration officer asked, very courteously, where she was born and how long she intended to stay in Detroit. She told him about the yellow ruffled curtains but he didn't seem interested.

For the first time in her life Mother stood on foreign soil and as she said afterwards she felt quite homesick. It gave her the queerest feeling to see people who looked and talked like Canadians, but weren't. Not of course, poor souls, that it was their fault.

She walked up Woodward Avenue, marveling at the number of recent-model cars on the street, for even prosperous Canadians drove their cars until they were worn out and none of this nonsense about trading in on a new model every year.

She passed the Gaiety and Avenue burlesque houses and their posters confirmed everything she had read in the Sunday supplements. But when she reached the shopping center, she forgave her neighbors every sin right back to and including the Revolutionary War.

Mother might be a staunch patriot, but she was fair. Eaton's and Simpson's might be the finest stores in all Canada, but they were not the equal of these. Best of all, she liked Crowley-Milner's. Crowley's had a magnificent escalator that carried one from floor to floor with no more effort than the stepping on, and moreover, from this vantage point, the entire contents of a department could be seen. Here she found exactly the curtains she wanted, and marked down, mind you, from $1.98 to $1.69.

Mother was completely happy. She marched back down

Woodward Avenue, pausing to admire the city hall, though its architecture was not the sort normally calculated to draw admiration. She stopped in at Vernor's for a glass of ginger ale, and boarded the ferryboat completely at peace with all mankind.

This frame of mind lasted until she reached the Canadian side.

When she got off the boat she was a little indignant when the Immigration officer asked her a lot of silly questions, just as if she were a foreigner. She was even more indignant when she was told she would have to pay thirty-eight cents duty on the curtains. Mother just couldn't believe her ears. She told the man about not being able to find the right shade of yellow in Windsor, but he said that didn't make any difference.

Mother had a sweet disposition but she could stick up for her rights. She told the Customs officer that we ought to remember the United States was our ally now and what would they think if they found out the Canadian Government was fining people for shopping in their country.

The Customs officer said in a tired voice that she could pay the duty or have the package confiscated.

Mother paid.

She went home mad as a wet hen. "That's what I get for being honest," she wailed to my father. "I didn't even have to show him those curtains. I could have put the package in my bag as easy as anything and he would never have known the difference."

Her voice trailed off. In her innocent blue eyes grew a

look such as Eve might have worn in the Garden of Eden
when she first started getting ideas about apples.

Next week Mother went shopping in Detroit again.

She came home with a new hat, a very elegant blue
brocade affair with a black plume.

"You can say what you like," she told my father, "but
American clothes have a lot more style to them."

Style was something on which Father was a little vague,
but he got right down to the really important matter.
"How much duty did you have to pay?" he asked.

Mother gave him a triumphant look. "Not a red cent,"
she gloated. "I wore over that old black straw that got
caught in the rain and just left it there and wore this
home."

Father was scandalized. "That's smuggling, Flora!" he
cried. "It's against the law."

"Show me the place in the Bible where it says a single
word about smuggling. Just show me," Mother declared,
confident that she was on solid ground, for she was a
staunch Baptist and, moreover, a total-immersion Baptist,
not one of those who intend to slide into Heaven with
only a sprinkling on the brow.

"Not the Bible," said Father patiently. "The law books.
You can't import goods into the country without paying
duty."

"Of all the nonsense," said Mother severely. "Do I go
running to Toronto to tell the Members of Parliament
where they can buy their sheets? I'll thank them to mind
their own business. Besides, I wasn't importing goods. I
was just buying a hat."

This logic left Father a trifle dazed but he tried to rally. "It isn't as if I lied," Mother continued virtuously. "As I was telling the minister's wife, if the Customs man had asked me about the hat, I would have told him the truth."

Father looked at her in horror. "You mean you told Mrs. Healy you smuggled a hat!"

Mother gave him a kind smile. "She was the one who told me to wear an old one across the border."

It is not to be wondered that Father felt a little confused. If there is one thing more than another on which Canadians pride themselves, it is that they are a highly law-abiding people. From that day on Father had his doubts—particularly about women.

For when it came to smuggling, Mother was by no means the only sinner. An observer sitting in the ferry waiting room might have been puzzled at the large number of women who walked through the door marked "Ladies" with parcel-laden arms and emerged some minutes later with empty hands and changed silhouettes.

It may be that the Canadian Customs men were too gallant to notice that their compatriots bulged in odd spots. At any rate unless a lady was carrying obvious merchandise in her hands, she was seldom stopped.

Father sent away for the new Eaton's and Simpson's catalogues, but Mother never took the trouble to remove the wrappers.

Even the smallpox scare didn't stop her. For a time everyone going through the American immigration office had to roll up his sleeve and display his vaccination scar. Mother for some reason had been vaccinated on her thigh. When the officer came to Mother she would blush furiously and whisper this information. They never asked for proof and this confirmed Mother's growing conviction that in spite of the Sunday supplements, Americans were very nice people.

There came a time when the Canadian Government, urged on by indignant Windsor merchants, decided to take steps. If the Customs officers were too reticent to enquire if a lady's bumps were real or artificial, then other means must be found.

The manner in which they solved this problem can only be described as underhanded.

They hired a woman Customs officer.

Mother came home from the Women's Institute in a

regular tizzy.

That Woman (she was never to refer to the female Customs officer by any other title)—that Woman had actually had the gall to order Mrs. Bernard Carmichael to step inside the Customs office and strip down to her underwear— No, not out in public, in a little room behind —and there was poor Mrs. Carmichael with a pair of silver salt shakers and a box of bubble bath in the legs of her pink rayon bloomers and a sugar-and-cream set tucked in her brassière. And that wasn't all. That Woman had examined the labels on Mrs. Carmichael's shoes and dress and made her pay double duty—$18.92—on everything.

Poor Mrs. Carmichael didn't have that much money with her and she began to cry because if they confiscated everything she would have to go home barefoot and in her slip (actually, Mother said, it's just a mercy she wasn't stripped as naked as the day she was born but there weren't labels in her underthings and That Woman couldn't prove anything). However, they let her phone Mr. Carmichael and he came and bailed her out but he lost half a day's work in addition to the $18.92 and he was fit to be tied and forbade her to set foot in Detroit again. Mr. Carmichael is Old Country and you know what Lords of Creation some of those Englishmen are. Poor Mrs. Carmichael didn't dare call her soul her own, even without the $18.92.

"But she did break the law," insisted my father. "I've warned you girls often enough you were going to get in trouble."

Then Mother, whose maternal uncle had been a member of the Buckingham Palace guard, said an incredibly shocking thing. "That Boston Tea Party," she muttered. "Sometimes I'm not a bit surprised."

The Women's Institute Members wrote an indignant protest against this unfair interference with their shopping privileges and sent it to the East Windsor Member of Parliament, but he was running for office on the slogan "Beer by the Glass" and was not very helpful.

That Woman continued to put in her appearance at the ferry dock and send innocent shoppers inside for inspection. The more timid women began to do their shopping in Windsor rather than risk embarrassment and double duty.

But not Mother. She became a little more careful about how she stowed her loot, but that was all.

When Mother was married she had had an eighteen-inch waist but over the years that had become a mere memory. This now turned out to be a distinct advantage. A skinny little thing like our neighbor Mrs. Martin might look as if she had sprouted outsize warts if she tried to bring a facecloth across the border, but no one even noticed if Mother swathed a sheet or so about her hips. Her crowning achievement was taking across a table lamp right under the snooping eyes of That Woman. I am not trying to explain how this was accomplished. I only know that she did.

Inevitably the day came when Mother was tapped on the arm and told to step inside the Customs office.

It was possibly the only time in all those years that she wasn't carrying some kind of contraband. She had gone over to buy a new dress and, not finding anything, returned empty-handed. Even the labels in her clothing had been cautiously removed for just such an emergency and replaced with old Eaton and Simpson ones. Mother submitted to being searched. Then quietly and with dignity, for she was always a lady, she told That Woman exactly what she thought of her and the entire Customs Department for persecuting innocent people. Ignoring all apologies, she swept in outraged virtue from the office.

It was around this time that I decided to marry an American and move to Detroit. Some of the relations said that surely there were enough fine young Canadian boys to go around, but Mother was all for it. Over the years the bonds of international friendship first engendered in Crowley's Department Store had grown. Mother had become quite fond of Americans. They had their little ways, like being too free and easy with divorce and not warming the pot before they made tea, but taken altogether, they were a warm-hearted, friendly people.

Mother came over regularly to Detroit to visit us and collected the life histories of her bus companions on the way. One week end when Father was to be out of town, she stayed for a few days.

She had bought a sandwich toaster (on sale at Crowley's for $3.98) and was trying to decide the best way to take it across past the prying eyes of That Woman.

I had a wonderful surprise for her. "Mother," I said,

"you don't have to smuggle it. When you stay on the American side for over twenty-four hours you can take back $50.00 worth of things duty free."

Mother just sniffed. "It'll be a fine day in the morning before *she* lets you take anything through free."

"I'll pay the duty if they charge you anything," I promised.

It took a lot of persuading.

That Woman was standing beside the pipe-lined passageways that divided up the commuters. When she saw the parcels in my mother's hands she gave her a curt nod to go inside.

"I told you so," Mother whispered to me. "I could have carried it down the neck of my dress as easy as anything."

She came out of the office wearing a slightly dazed look.

"I didn't have to pay any duty," she said. She walked up the hill to Ouellette Avenue without saying a word.

"After all these years," she repeated again. "No duty." For a woman who had just been freed from a life of crime, she didn't look very happy.

"Remember the time I no more than got through the Customs when that alarm clock I had hidden in my bloomer leg started ringing," she said wistfully.

In her mind, I think, she was recalling every illicit pillow case and hairpin she had brought across—that last reckless glimpse in the ferry mirror to be certain there were no unreasonable obtrusions—the swift beat of the heart as the danger zone was approached—a wonderful, terror-stricken moment, and then safety.

It was all over now. Never again would she live dangerously.

For the first time in years she stopped to look in the window of one of Windsor's department stores. "Have you noticed how much more stylish their things are getting over here?" she asked.

"They're all right," I agreed. "Isn't it nice, Mother, you'll be able to bring over your winter coat without any trouble."

She caught my arm. "That blue dress in the window— It's been marked down from twenty-nine dollars— I wonder if they have it in my size."

"But Mother—" I protested.

"It would please your father," she said firmly. "You know he has never approved of buying things across the border. Besides, you can say what you like, but there's nothing quite as good as our Canadian woollens."

Without as much as a backward glance at the siren spires of Detroit, she went inside the store.

· T H R E E ·

The Garden in the Bathtub

While Mother's lawless behavior was an occasional
problem, we had our troubles with Father too.

Father was a handsome, quiet man who had been
known to say that with six women around he never got a
chance to talk. Actually he was of English-Irish-Scottish
descent in about equal proportions, but he was fond of
the bagpipes and to hear him tell it you would have
thought he had just erupted from the heather. Father was
a Scotsman who had never seen his chosen land.

He could be stubborn too, and it complicated our lives
considerably when he decided to grow tomatoes in the
bathtub. In a family with five daughters, this was something of an inconvenience, even if it was for our own good.

One day Father looked around our big, solid home with
its adequate heating system and well-upholstered furniture
and knew that he had been a failure as a parent.

We were too comfortable.

Deep in the British soul is engrained the belief that
there is something very virtuous about hardship. None of
this pampering of food with sauces and seasonings as the

French do. Boil the stuff until it is limp, tasteless and un-resisting. Sleep in unheated bedrooms. Get up early in the morning and take a cold bath.

Wear goose pimples instead of a halo.

Generally Father was the most indulgent of parents but every so often some trifle like pale pink bathroom tissue would send him off in a regular dither. When he was a boy, he said (and you could almost see the hair sprouting on his chest) he had gone into the northern woods equipped only with an ax and his trusty rifle. He had slept on cedar boughs beneath the open sky and lived on game and fish.

When Father started that line, it was run for cover, girls. Someone's character was going to get developed.

The affair of the tomato plants caught us off guard be-cause it happened in the wintertime. After all, even Father couldn't expect us to take a trusty ax and go sleep on pine boughs with the temperature around zero. Be-sides, we had noticed as the years passed that Father was much more apt to talk about sleeping under the open sky than actually do it.

It started on account of the cans in the trash pile. Every family in Canada and the United States has cans in the trash pile, but all at once Father got excited about it.

The funny part was he didn't blame Mother. He never did. Mother was perfect, and sometimes he said sadly none of us would ever be the woman she was. Modesty, I think, kept him from adding because we wouldn't be able to marry men like him, but he didn't say so. He just worried because we weren't developing any character.

He put the cans up in a row (there did seem to be an awful lot of them)—canned peas, canned corn, canned peaches. When he was young, he said, and then he stopped. Even to his loving eye it was only too apparent that none of us girls was apt to be handy with an ax or a rifle.

We girls, he went on sadly, were incapable of coping with nature in the raw. Before it was too late, we must learn to face the realities of life. If nothing else, we were going to learn how to grow our own food.

The fact that the middle of a lusty Canadian winter is hardly the time to start a vegetable garden bothered him not at all. Father throve on problems.

Up until now the bathroom had been one of the pleasantest rooms in the house, with a large window overlooking the Detroit River, a wicker rocking-chair and a well-stocked bookcase.

Suddenly the house reeked to high heaven with chemicals. The bathtub was filled with a witch's brew topped by a screen of wire mesh and excelsior in which were embedded several small green plants. Father assembled us in a row to admire his handiwork. This was something called hydroponic gardening. It was, he proclaimed happily, the greatest advance in agriculture since the Garden of Eden. No digging, no weeding—nothing to do but sit back and wait for the harvest.

"But how about baths?" we cried. "It's all very well to be self-sufficient, but you've got to be sanitary too."

Father looked very reproving. When he was young, he said, every Saturday night he thawed out the pump, carried water a quarter of a mile, heated it on a wood-burning stove and scrubbed himself by the open oven with one side of him roasting and the other side freezing.

We knew when we were licked. We left before Father decided to improve our characters by moving the rest of the plumbing fixtures outside.

We appealed to Mother, but for once, she let us down. "It isn't often your father gets a notion," she said, "and I think it would be nice to let him have his own way and get it over with. Besides," she added, "I was full grown before I had a bath myself—in a regular bathtub, that is. It won't hurt you a bit."

We developed our self-reliance by bringing an old round zinc washtub up from the basement. Senna, who was the artistic member of the family, painted it white and decorated it with pink roses. While she was at it, she added a few intertwined buds to the patch on the toilet basin which had been accidentally cracked by a shotgun blast the last time Aunt Lucy visited us.

There was nothing left now but to keep a stiff upper lip and see it through.

The garden grew like mad, the stems a little thin because the winter light was not too good, but in no time at all the entire tub was a mass of vegetation with roots like the tentacles of an octopus. I don't know if I can explain, but the whole effect was somehow evil.

Here was this ordinary bathtub in an ordinary house

with such an extraordinary content. The plants themselves did not have the solid honesty of plants grown in
soil and I always had an uneasy, embarrassed feeling that
something might be leering out at me from that strange
junglelike growth. I used the bathroom only in case of
dire necessity and my sisters did the same.

Indeed, even if one had the desire, it was becoming in-
creasingly difficult to get in the bathroom. Father seemed
to have entirely forgotten that we were the ones who were
supposed to learn how to raise our own food.

He was an indefatigable gardener. Business was slack
at that time of year so he spent hour after hour bending
over the tub, adding strange, fearful-smelling potions to
the brew, snipping off a yellowing leaf here, a stem there.
Worse than that, he kept showing the garden to visitors.
You would have thought we were running a regular
Cook's Tour. It got so a girl didn't dare roam around upstairs in her own home without all her clothes on, for fear
she might run into a total stranger wanting to see the
garden in the bathtub.

Weeks passed, and we began to grow desperate. We
even considered such a frantic measure as pulling out the
plug and letting the fluid escape, though personally I
would rather have died or gone bathless for life than put
my hand into that unholy foliage.   .

In a way, what happened next was Father's fault. He
had decided that it was time Senna and I helped him with
his accounts. Trying to keep books for Father was like
nothing on earth. He had a fabulous memory for figures

Vasiliu

and he carried everything in his head. It was a matter of surprise and regret to him that Senna and I seemed to have failed to inherit this intuitive quality. We needed facts and figures to keep accurate books, a weakness which Father blamed on modern education.

Senna and I went down to Ripley's hardware to see if Father's account there would help us straighten out the mess. While Senna went over the bills, I read the labels on cans. How to kill roaches—how to remove paint—Weedo.

I asked Mr. Ripley about it. (Mr. Ripley was a short, stout man, with a short, stout wife, and he had four short, stout children and a dachshund dog.)

"It's a new idea," Mr. Ripley said. "Supposed to do away with all the bother of weeding. Just spray this stuff on instead. Works fine on grass they say, but you have to be careful in gardens. Kills some plants as well as weeds."

Senna and I looked at each other. I suppose when you think of it, that is how murder is born. Desperation—the opportunity—

"Do you know if it would hurt tomatoes?" we asked.

That evening while Senna kept watch, I crept into the bathroom. For a moment I stood there trembling, looking down into that sinister, green, growing mass. My hand shook so that I could scarcely uncork the bottle. Only the memory of the days when that tub had been a proper piece of equipment filled with bubble bath sustained me. I jerked the cork out and dumped the contents of the bottle all at once into the brew in the bathtub. The fatal deed was accomplished.

A spot of chemical had fallen on my hand. I rubbed and rubbed like Lady Macbeth. Out! Out! Damned spot!

Senna had her head in the linen closet weeping and hiccoughing—she always got hiccoughs when she was excited. "You shouldn't have done it!" she sobbed. "You shouldn't have done it!"

It was too late now.

We ducked out of sight into our own bedroom and hid the bottle under the mattress along with a copy of *Lady Chatterley's Lover* (which we had found quite dull) when we heard Father coming up the stairs with Mr. Higgins, a lumber dealer out Wyandotte Street (Mr. Higgins was a little bald man who always used to put a silver dollar in the collection plate at church).

Senna and I got down on the floor and put our ears next to the hot-air register. We could hear the rumble of their voices, but not what they were saying.

Suddenly Father gave a great shout. "Flora—Vicki—Senna—Lee— All of you! Come here! Come here at once!"

Senna and I turned pale and clutched each other. She began to hiccough again.

"It couldn't have worked that fast!" I whispered.

When we reached the bathroom, the plants still rose in lush greenness, but Father was standing in the middle of the blue linoleum floor, snapping his suspenders and beaming from ear to ear. Mr. Higgins stood reverently behind him.

"Girls," said Father, "I want you to remember this moment as long as you live. Time after time I have told you that any problem can be solved if you go at it in a practical way."

I wondered what he would think when he found out how Senna and I had solved our particular problem.

Father pointed a proud finger. "What do you think of that?"

Dangling from one of the tomato plants like a Christmas ornament was a small green ball.

"Let me be the first to congratulate you," Mr. Higgins said to my father. "I wouldn't be a bit surprised if the *Border Cities Star* would be interested in a little item about this achievement."

Back in our own room Senna and I looked at each other. "I feel," I moaned, "like a murderer."

"Maybe the weed killer won't work," Senna said; but we both knew better.

Within a couple of days the leaves of the tomato plants began to curl at the edges and turn yellow.

That week end Father scarcely left the bathroom, but he looked so unhappy that in spite of the inconvenience not one of us complained.

Day after day, we saw him, whenever he had a few minutes home, adding a bit of fluid, snipping off a curled brown leaf, tying back the yellow chintz drapes so as to allow a little more light, but in vain.

As if in a last frenzied fight for survival, the single tomato grew and grew, turning a sad gold that deepened into a promise of crimson.

Then abruptly, all was over. Coming home from school one afternoon, I glanced in the bathroom and saw the shriveled, drying stalks stretched on the chicken-wire bier. Among them glowed, like a memory, the half-ripened fruit. Father stood beside the tub, his broad shoulders drooping. I couldn't stand it any more.

Father seldom lost his temper, but when he did, he made up for it. I didn't care. Even if he disowned me, I had to confess what I had done.

He didn't believe me until I showed him the empty bottle.

"So that's what happened," he said grimly.

I waited for the heavens to open up.

Senna, who had heard the commotion, came hiccoughing up the stairs, sobbing that it was her fault too.

Father put down the bottle and looked at us with the bewildered look he sometimes wore when contemplating his female offspring. Then his big arms gathered us tenderly, awkwardly to him. "There, there, Little Ones," he said. "All the tomatoes in the world aren't worth those tears."

"We'll sleep on the floor in sleeping bags," we wept. "We'll take weaving at school and learn to make our own clothes."

Father put a desperate hand into his trouser pocket and took out a handful of change. "Stop crying, both of you," he begged. "Now go on over to the drugstore and get yourselves two of those ice-cream dishes with a lot of stuff on top."

It seemed an odd way to develop our character, but surely Father knew best.

When we came back the smell of chemicals had gone from the bathroom as completely as if it had never existed and the tub gleamed, pristine as country snow.

Senna and I tossed a nickel to see who would have the first bubble bath.

At dinner that night Jenny, our mother's helper, brought in a small silver dish on which reposed four slices of watery, half-ripened tomato. She passed it around twice, but no one was very hungry.

FOUR

The Baby in the Anglican Overcoat

In most respects ours was a sedate, middle-class neighborhood. Our neighbor to the left was Dr. Healy, the Anglican minister.

Dr. Healy was a kindly, nearsighted man with a shock of heavy white hair. He owned an ancient Plymouth, and when he drove he put his faith in the Lord and no nonsense about stop streets or red lights. Some people said that they didn't know if his sermons had converted many, but his driving certainly started a lot of people thinking about the hereafter.

Even in a bathing suit, he looked like a good man. He was very fond of the water, and during the summer he used to work on his sermons on a raft that he had made by lashing planks to oil drums. It was quite an ingenious affair with a red beach umbrella and a place for a thermos of lemonade and a box of Fig Newtons, of which he was very fond.

One day the raft broke loose from the dock where it was anchored, but he was so busy writing he never even noticed until he had drifted so far downriver he was about

35

to collide with the Detroit-Windsor ferry.

Mrs. Healy was Mother's best friend. She labored under the delusion that she was the hardheaded member of the Healy family. "People," she was fond of saying, "simply take advantage of Ron's good nature." (Ron was Dr. Healy.) And indeed it was true.

"Now take this afternoon," I remember hearing her say. "That useless Mat Kerner came around and asked him for five dollars so his youngsters could go to the circus." (Mat Kerner was the one who used to leave his teeth on the stairpost when he had been drinking.)

"Five dollars!" said Mrs. Healy, "For once I put my foot down." She paused triumphantly. "I told him I thought three dollars would be plenty."

Both Mother and Mrs. Healy were the kind of woman who couldn't bear to be idle. When they sat on the terrace to talk, they darned old socks for the poor, which Mrs. Healy collected from her husband's congregation (Father once said that the difference between the Anglicans and the Baptists was that we Baptists had to wear out our own darned socks).

The river front was a good two miles from the railroad tracks, but word must have gotten around, for all during the depression down-and-outers who rode the rods knew that either one house or the other was good for a meal and a neatly darned pair of socks.

Mrs. Healy wasn't, however, a very good cook, or rather she was a somewhat absent-minded one and was apt to let things burn dry. Almost any summer day the smell of scorched potatoes would drift through the air along with the scent of Dr. Healy's flowers.

Pierre Laframboise was our neighbor to the right. Mr. Laframboise was bald headed and short, with long arms and a powerful chest that seemed to have been intended for a larger man. He was a good-natured soul, who loved his huge family, and indeed all children. He was also an enthusiastic gardener and people came from all around to see his roses.

By profession he was a bootlegger. He was a bootlegger, just as some men are lawyers or bankers, and indeed seemed to feel that he rendered a distinct service to the community. He was a conscientious bootlegger who took pride in his craft. It was true, he admitted to my father, that he sometimes procured a bottle or two for a friend, as who did not, but the quality was of the finest, not cut with wood alcohol.

"One can drink my whiskey certain he will not lose the eyesight," he used to boast.

There were, however, some hazards and inconveniences connected with his job. Every now and then he would be arrested and obliged to spend time in jail, playing pinochle with the local chief of police, who happened to be a cousin of his. From these comfortable quarters he used to dispatch voluminous messages to my father and Dr. Healy, exhorting them, as good neighbors, to keep an eye on his garden and his family.

It says much for the tolerance and good will of all concerned, as well as the staunch buffer qualities of my mother and father, that, in spite of their disapproval of each other's mode of living (and the disapproval was mutual), the Healys and the Laframboises were able to stay on neighborly terms.

Mrs. Laframboise was a warm-hearted, handsome woman, who wore earrings and high heels even when she did the wash.

She was terribly afraid of lightning storms and while she relied on her patron saint to do her best for her, she wasn't taking any chances. She had an enormous feather bed with its legs fitted into pans of water which she believed acted as insulators and when it stormed, she and the children took refuge under the covers.

As a matter of fact, whether it was Mrs. Laframboise's saints or Dr. Healy's prayers, when our community was struck by a tornado, it swerved out in a loop like a fence around our three homes, leaving them completely unharmed, though the surrounding district suffered severe damage.

At regular intervals, with a somewhat triumphant air, Mrs. Laframboise produced children. On this particular occasion, however, she chose a very inconvenient time for her accouchement.

In the first place her husband was being unavoidably detained for some thirty days in the local jail. My father too was out of town (though not for the same reason). It was necessary, therefore, for Dr. Healy to drive her to the hospital. Even in good weather, Dr. Healy's driving was on the erratic side and this was in the middle of the worst snowstorm of the year.

Mrs. Healy stayed with the weeping Laframboise brood.

"We're going to have a lovely time, children," she said. "We'll make popcorn and cookies, and when your mother comes home again, she'll have a lovely surprise for you."

The Laframboise children stopped weeping and surveyed her with a wondering pitying air. It was obvious she must be completely ignorant of certain simple facts of life and they proceeded to enlighten her with accurate frankness. Mrs. Healy who had been brought up in a period when babies were found in cabbage patches was so confused she put chop-suey sauce instead of vanilla in the cookies.

In the meantime the Plymouth was gallantly slewing its way to the hospital, with Dr. Healy crouched over the wheel as if it were a live thing that might get away, and Mother in the back seat urging him to hurry.

Mrs. Laframboise was never one to suffer in silence and she rather prided herself on having her babies at the top of her lungs.

Dr. Healy did his best to concentrate on his driving and ignore the commotion in the back seat, but the weather was too much for him and about a block from the hospital, the car skidded into a snowbank. By then it was too late anyhow.

He made the rest of the trip on foot, floundering through the drifts and bearing in his arms an eight-pound Roman Catholic baby boy wrapped up in an Anglican overcoat.

Physically neither mother nor child was the worse for the adventure (and it supplied Mrs. Laframboise with conversational ammunition for years). Spiritually, however, it was a very upsetting affair.

Poor devout Mrs. Laframboise was inconsolable. Father Campeau, who had been summoned immediately to baptize the child, did his best to reassure her that the boy was not lost to the Church by reason of this enforced contact with Protestant clergy. He promised if necessary to take it up with the bishop himself.

Mrs. Laframboise continued to weep. "Colette, my first," she wailed, "was born maybe five-six months after we marry—but we were so young and everyone knows how those things will happen, but this—mon dieu, how can I ever look anyone in the face!"

Dr. Healy, whose intentions had been of the kindest, was quite embarrassed. In order to spare Mrs. Laframboise's feelings, he gave the overcoat to the Salvation Army, though it was a good one that had only been worn four years.

It was not, you understand, that the Laframboise family was ungrateful. Mr. Laframboise consulted with my father as to whether it might be proper to present Dr. Healy with a good case of Scotch as a token of esteem. When Father vetoed this, the entire family went shopping, returning with a happy air to bestow on Dr. and Mrs. Healy an enormous picture of a forest fire, lighted through the back by a flickering lamp. Rather than hurt their feelings, Dr. Healy, who had never quite been able to accept the Impressionists, installed it over the mantel in place of a fine Romney reproduction.

Every time he looked at that Dante's Inferno of artistic triumph, he must have wished he had left le petit Alphonse in the snowbank.

As a matter of fact, so did the neighbors.

That Alphonse was a holy terror. He used to ride his sled down the front stairs, right over the good green Axminster carpeting with red roses, and once he tried to flush the cat down the toilet.

Vasiliu

But while the other children were firmly disciplined, Alphonse was allowed to do as he pleased.

"After all," Mrs. Laframboise would shrug, "it is not his fault, pauvre enfant. He was born in sin."

·FIVE·

Fare and Warmer

Not all the neighbors were quite as colorful as Mr. and Mrs. Laframboise, though Mr. and Mrs. Wilton were close seconds. Mrs. Wilton was a thin woman with a figure like a wire coathanger and a nervous trick of clearing her throat. She and Mr. Wilton didn't get along too well, and when she was mad at him she used to starch his shorts and socks when she did the laundry.

Mr. Wilton had an interesting hobby. He used to send greeting cards to people whom he didn't know. When things were slack at the store, he read the newspaper, making notes of the people to whom he might send cards. He sent cards of congratulation to Eagle Scouts, beauty-contest winners, newly elected club presidents and the growers of prize tomatoes. He was completely democratic. He sent King George a card on his proper birth date (not the one selected by Parliament) and he sent cards to Jack Dempsey, the garbage man and Greta Garbo.

As a matter of fact, Mr. Wilton wasn't the only person in our neighborhood who had a hobby. Mr. Roger Dickensheet, who had been a watch repairman, used to print

43

the Lord's Prayer on grains of rice, and Aunt Addie collected chicken wishbones.

Aunt Addie wasn't really our aunt. She was a widowed neighbor who lived in a white house crammed with ferneries. She used to write to celebrities like Mary Garden and Babe Ruth and ask them to save a chicken wishbone for her. These she painted with gilt and anchored to the wall of her bedroom with velvet ribbons (blue for men, pink for ladies).

She was a plump, kindly little soul with nearsighted brown eyes who loved everyone and everything on earth except the street railway system.

Aunt Addie's feud with the street railway, and in particular with street-car conductors, dated back to 1921 when one of them let her get off at East Grand Boulevard instead of East Grand Avenue in a pouring rain and ruin a new Easter hat with silver metallic embroidery. Nothing could ever convince Aunt Addie that this deed was not committed with malice aforethought.

After that she always sat up in the little seat just back of the motorman and every few minutes she would poke him and ask if the next street was Dundee. It got so that street-car motormen who recognized Aunt Addie would go right by a whole safety zone of people rather than risk being poked black and blue.

Not content with poking the motorman, whom she by no means trusted, or asking advice of her neighbors, Aunt Addie also listened to the street-car conductor. When he called out a particularly long, unintelligible list of streets, she would ring the bell and elbow her way to the exit calling, "Coming through! Coming through!" in a desperate voice.

She never remembered to have her fare ready, and at the box, she would block the exit while she pawed furiously through the aspirin boxes and old letters in the black calf bag her late husband had given her as an anniversary present, until at last she found seven cents. All the time she was hunting, Aunt Addie would keep insisting to the conductor, "Is this Dundee? Is this Dundee?" If the conductor said, "No," Aunt Addie got off anyway.

As soon as she was in the safety zone she would recognize that it was not her stop and run to the front of the car and pound the door for the motorman to let her on. Once again she would occupy the seat behind him and in a few minutes the entire process would be repeated with the conductor loudly insisting that Aunt Addie pay her fare and Aunt Addie insisting, not loud but firm, that she already had paid it. The inevitable result of this procedure was that Aunt Addie would be carried six blocks past her stop and reach home in a very bitter state of mind.

Rather than risk the perils of the public transportation system, Aunt Addie took her pleasures near home. She went to the neighborhood movie, seeing each feature twice and closing her eyes at the sad parts. She loved auction sales, never raising a bid more than a dime and sometimes getting stuck with odd items like harness clamps or chipped gravy boats.

On sunny afternoons she often took a bag of peanuts

and strolled the few blocks to Riverview Park. Here she would seat herself on a green bench under one of the big elms and feed the pigeons, smiling happily as they cooed and waddled about in a manner somewhat reminiscent of Aunt Addie herself in her fur-trimmed winter galoshes.

One fine June day Aunt Addie realized that every Thursday afternoon the pigeons were fed from a nearby bench by a pleasant, middle-aged man, shaped much like one of those roly-poly toys that bob up when pushed over. With pleasure and some confusion, Aunt Addie began to notice that the little man was much more interested in her than in the pigeons.

On the following Thursday, though actually it was movie rather than park weather, Aunt Addie bought an even larger bag of peanuts and went to the park. The stranger was waiting and Aunt Addie pretended not to notice that his bench had been moved mysteriously several feet closer to hers.

Each Thursday found the benches coming closer and closer until at last they nestled side by side as cozy as a pair of cupcakes in a cellophane package.

One afternoon Aunt Addie accidentally spilled her purse and the man picked up her glasses case, a piece of green watered silk that she meant to match, a yo-yo (a game at which she was quite proficient), a broken lead pencil and four wire hairpins.

His name was Wilfred Rumple and as Aunt Addie put it, the two of them took to each other from the first. Apparently Mr. Rumple considered that, though silent, his

courtship had been sufficient and on the following Thursday, he asked Aunt Addie to marry him. Aunt Addie had every intention of accepting, but she didn't want to act as if she were in too big a rush.

It was, she said later, the most romantic thing, with the coal barges drifting by and the pigeons cooing (though sometimes of course they are the messiest things).

Mr. Rumple placed his qualifications before her like a real gentleman. He was a churchgoing man (Presbyterian), a widower with two married children on the coast. He owned his own home—he showed her a picture—had a comfortable bank account—he presented the book—and had a good steady job.

Aunt Addie was weakening fast, but she tried to be practical. "What do you do, Wilfred?" she asked.

Mr. Rumple patted a stray dog with a kindly, absent-minded hand. "I'm a street-car conductor. Been on the Benbow line for the last twelve years."

Aunt Addie felt faint all over. She couldn't believe her ears. She just couldn't believe her ears. "A street-car conductor!" she echoed in a shocked voice.

Mr. Rumple looked hurt. "It's a good steady job," he protested. "Keeps me off my bunions and I meet a nice class of people. I *like* being a street-car conductor."

Aunt Addie got to her feet, scattering the peanuts on the ground. "I—I'll have to think it over," she choked and rushed from the park leaving Mr. Rumple alone with the pigeons.

As soon as she got home, Aunt Addie came over to see

our mother, who she felt was an authority on men.

"I thought I could trust him," Aunt Addie wept. "We had so much in common, both of us liking hobbies." (Mr. Rumple collected spider webs, which he sprayed with lacquer and mounted in boxes.)

"I'll make you a good strong cup of tea," said Mother. (Mother thought a good strong cup of tea was a sure cure for everything from fallen arches to a broken heart.)

Aunt Addie's tears dribbled into the orange pekoe. "A person has to draw the line someplace, and you know what street-car conductors are! You just can't trust them."

Mother understood Aunt Addie's feelings perfectly. As a matter of fact, she herself felt something the same way about the post office. If we missed getting any mail in a delivery, she was always secretly convinced that it was because the postal employees just didn't have their hearts in their work.

"All the same," she said to Aunt Addie, "if you really feel you love Mr. Rumple, you should try to understand his viewpoint."

Next afternoon Aunt Addie came chugging up our steps. "I did as you said, Flora," she cried. "I took your advice. I got on Wilfred's car without him knowing so I could watch him, at work."

"I always like to look at people on street cars," Mother said. "You see such interesting characters."

"He looks nice and neat in his uniform," Aunt Addie reported. "He'd be ever so handsome if he had a little hair."

Mother snipped a dead leaf from a geranium. (She was a chronic leaf snipper and she also liked to straighten pictures.) "Hair isn't everything," she said.

Aunt Addie wasn't even listening. "He has a mind of his own," she went on. "I like a man that's got some gumption. Most of the time he was ever so pleasant, but a fat woman got on with a kid almost as big as I am and tried to say he was only five, but Wilfred, calm as anything, made the boy stand beside the measuring bar and he was a good eight inches over and for all her snippiness, he just waited until the mother paid an extra fare."

"Some people try to get away with anything," said Mother.

"Then a man got on with a transfer that was two hours old. He wasn't so tough when Wilfred got through with him. Polite, you know, but firm."

Mother got down to the really important issue. "What happened when Mr. Rumple saw you?"

Aunt Addie blushed. "We got engaged while we were waiting at the car barn. We're going to be married next month. With a job like his that poor boy needs someone to see he eats properly. Wouldn't you think the least some women could do is have their fare ready instead of blocking the aisle?"

A Drop of Auntie's Ruin

A romance like Aunt Addie's was just the sort of thing Mother enjoyed. There was nothing she liked better than marrying people off. It was one of the reasons we changed hired help so often.

It would be completely presumptuous to refer to the girls who helped Mother around the house as maids. They were treated like members of the family—though not a bit better. Most of them were English or Scottish girls, newly arrived from the Old Country—Mother wasn't too fond of the Irish, who were apt, she felt, to be a bit sketchy about the corners.

Of all the girls, the one we remember with the most affection was Jenny Higgins.

The thing that bothered Jenny most when she came to work for us was that Father buttered his own bread. In time she came to accept the fact that the family actually opened the morning paper before Father had seen it, and that on a chilly morning he was the one who got the furnace going. But it was hard for her to believe that Mother could be completely guilty of shirking her wifely duty and sometimes as she passed the breakfast things there was a faint note of reproach in her soft English voice.

It was plain she was thinking that back home her own Dadda would never put up with such nonsense.

We had known Jenny's parents from the days when they came to Canada from the Old Country with not much more than they wore on their backs.

Mrs. Higgins and the five little ones had been sick the entire crossing but Dadda was made of sterner stuff. " 'e 'eld our 'eads over the basin the 'ole way," his wife reported proudly. "Got a stomach strong as a 'orse."

The family arrived in Windsor, utterly destitute, though not at all downhearted. Our mother, who had heard about them from the minister, persuaded Father to give Dadda a job to tide them over.

It was characteristic of Mrs. Higgins, who appreciated the proper status of the male in the world, that she always gave the credit for their rescue to Father rather than Mother.

Dadda was a halfpint of a man with a balding head. Mrs. Higgins was built along the lines of a wrestler. But there was no question about who ruled the roost in that house. What Dadda said, went.

At Jenny's home no matter how late or how early Dadda might be in coming home, his supper was supposed to be hot and ready. Mrs. Higgins used to post one of the small tykes down the street to give her warning of Dadda's approach. At the signal, the house vibrated like a battleship preparing for action. Plates went into the warming oven and fresh water into the teakettle. The largest piece of pie, the choicest bits of meat, were Dadda's by feudal right. Later, it was he who sat in the most comfortable chair with the earphones of the crystal radio set clamped on a head as shining as his wife's best china.

There was, however, nothing of the tyrant about Dadda. He was a kindly, good-natured little man, addicted to braces and an outsize hat. It was only in the adoring eyes of his family that he loomed a six-foot monarch.

Jenny was sixteen when she came to work for us. Jenny didn't look like a Higgins. The rest of the family were short and chirpy as sparrows. Jenny was slim and quiet with an exquisite English complexion, and soft dark hair.

In my romantic soul I was positive that she didn't really belong to the Higginses. Mrs. Higgins had been in service and I believed she had switched babies and Jenny was actually the long-lost daughter of the earl (Mrs. Higgins was so obviously respectable that any other solution never occurred to me). It was an interesting thought and I used to wonder if the old earl felt like a robin with a cowbird in its nest whenever he heard the changeling Higgins dropping h's around his castle.

Jenny liked living with us, once she got used to our peculiar ways, though at first she did insist on having Father's slippers warmed and waiting for him when he came home. Father, whose feet were as hardy as the rest of him (he also had double-jointed toes), had never worn slippers around the house in his life and declined to start now, even to please Jenny.

Jenny was a sweet, polite girl and she did her best to

hide her disapproval of our behavior, but once when Bonnie had kept one of her boy friends waiting even longer than usual, Jennie murmured that she wondered how Canadian girls ever got husbands. (My sister Bonnie was the prettiest one of the family. Every time she fell in love, she washed her hair. She had the cleanest scalp in town, though her hair wouldn't have been so blond if she hadn't used all that lemon juice.)

Jenny herself had a young man—Tom Henderson was his name. He was a clean-looking, stocky lad with bright blue eyes. Like Jenny, he was English, and like her Dadda, he felt it was a man's world. When he came to call, Jenny was supposed to be ready and waiting with her hat on. Moreover, his idea of showing her a good time was to take her for a walk in the rain. Being favored with his company was supposed to be enough of a treat, though sometimes he did loosen up to the extent of bringing her a slightly wilted bouquet from the florist shop where he was a clerk.

Life in Canada was undoubtedly topsy-turvy but not even my father's struggle to retain his masculine privileges against five daughters had entirely prepared Jennie for the Ellsworths.

The Ellsworths were an American family who had taken the house next to us for the summer. Mr. Ellsworth was a Ford Motor executive, a fact that impressed Jenny not a little since Dadda was now employed at the Canadian branch.

Mr. Ellsworth was a big, imposing man with a fine head

of hair. Mrs. Ellsworth was as slim and pretty as her own eighteen-year-old daughter.

One evening shortly after the new family moved in, Jennie happened to glance towards their kitchen. Mr. Ellsworth with a ruffled apron tied about his rotund middle was wiping dishes.

Jenny was so shocked she dropped one of Mother's crystal goblets.

Ordinarily Jenny minded her own business with proper English reticence, but now she frankly snooped. What she discovered left her in a state of emotional confusion— Mr. Ellsworth not only got his own breakfast—he took a cup of coffee into his wife's bedroom.

At first Jenny thought Mrs. Ellsworth might be the victim of a heart condition or some mysterious ailment. Mrs. Ellsworth disproved this by playing tennis every afternoon. She went shopping and came home long after Mr. Ellsworth's dinner hour with the car full of extravagant parcels.

Yet in spite of all this undutiful behavior, it was obvious that the Ellsworths were a very devoted, happy couple. Jenny was completely baffled.

"I guess it's just different people having different ways," she decided charitably at last. "Like some of the heathen having half a dozen wives."

It was right around this time we began to notice that Jenny was acting a little odd. She began to stand out in the back yard looking across the Detroit River to the American side and occasionally talking to herself.

One evening when Tom Henderson came to call for her, she wasn't ready. Tom waited fifteen minutes, then left in a huff.

When Jenny came down (actually she had been dressed all this time, but had sat in her room looking at the clock) she was quite provoked.

"The airs of him," she sniffed. "You'd think he was a Lord of Creation."

"Tom's a fine boy, Jenny," Mother reminded her. "He has his little ways, but he is doing well at the shop."

"Don't you think working in a florist's is sort of romantic?" Bonnie asked.

"Not very," said Jennie. "He shovels manure."

She stared across the Detroit River again. "I," she said, "am going to marry an American."

Not, it soon developed, any particular American, but she wasn't going to marry a Canadian because they didn't make enough money and she certainly wasn't going to marry an Englishman.

"Do you know," she said earnestly, "that every single meal my Mums butters Dadda's bread for him. He always eats two slices. How many pieces do you think she must have buttered in twenty years?"

There was a shattering silence while we tried to picture the mountainous pile of bread buttered by the loyal hands of Mrs. Higgins.

"Your father and mother are one of the happiest couples I know," Mother reminded her gently.

Jenny tossed her pretty head. "Mums likes to wait on

him," she said. "She thinks it's the proper way to act, but I'm going to marry an American and let him wait on me."

Next week Jenny left us, and her sister Annie took her place. Annie was a good-natured girl, and a willing worker, but she was a true Higgins and no daughter of the earl. She dropped her h's and occasionally the teacups and she was always waiting with her hat on when Tom Henderson asked her out.

Jenny's strange ideas caused considerable commotion in her home.

"It's against nature, that's wot it is," Mrs. Higgins declared. "You don't see the lions and chickens getting such notions."

"The whole trouble with the United States is too many women running things," Dadda agreed. "Wouldn't surprise me a bit if they 'ad a woman President some day."

"How about Queen Victoria," Jenny began.

"None of your lip, young lady," said Mrs. Higgins. "If you find a man 'alf as good as your father, you'll be proud to butter 'is bread."

All the same, they didn't raise any objections when Jenny got a job in Detroit clerking at the J. L. Hudson store. Immigration regulations at that time were very lenient—indeed half of Windsor worked over in Detroit, commuting back and forth on the ferry.

Jenny earned fifteen dollars a week—later she was raised to eighteen—and she was very pleased with her job. She worked at the candy counter selling chocolate-coated marshmallows, imitation orange slices and maraschino cherries. The first month she was always ducking below the counter to nibble. Fortunately for her complexion and figure, she got so she couldn't stand the sight of candy.

At Christmas, using her employee discount, she bought splendidly extravagant presents, not only for her own family, but for ours. She had an endearing way of buying the most utterly inappropriate gifts. She gave my mother a pair of red, shirred-satin garters trimmed with ostrich feathers. Mother treasured them for years, though she only wore them that once. They were indeed one of her few possessions we were never able to borrow.

Day by day Jenny seemed to grow prettier. Her clothes began to acquire a look of American smartness. She bought a lipstick. With a skin like hers, it was all the make-up she needed.

Occasionally she double dated with girls at the store and went dancing at the Graystone or the Arcadia, or on a moonlight excursion to Boblo. Sometimes she still went out with Tom, though their date usually ended in a quarrel.

"He doesn't know the first thing about showing a girl a good time," Jenny complained. "We never see anything except Westerns because that's the only kind of picture Tom likes. I'd ever so much rather see Valentino."

By now Jenny had met quite a few American men, but while some of them had ideas, they weren't quite what Jenny had in mind.

She thought things over, and instead of dancing evenings, she went to night school and took a business course.

Her typing was good, her shorthand and spelling a little sketchy. She got a job for $22.00 a week, working for a young lawyer who had just opened up his office in the Buhl Building.

She brought her boss over to see us. Frank Mallard seemed a nice, intelligent young fellow, perfectly capable of buttering his own bread. Moreover, he was an American.

"Don't you think," Jenny said later, "that Frank—Mr. Mallard—looks a little like Valentino?"

Since Frank was sandy haired and wore glasses, the resemblance was a trifle elusive.

"No good will come out of it," said Tom darkly. "Spendin' money like water. I know 'is kind."

"And I suppose," said Jenny pertly, "you're only interested in my lovely soul."

Tom turned a shattered crimson, and Bonnie and I looked at him with surprise and interest. Lust of the flesh was somehow something we had never connected with Tom.

Jenny's boss took her to see the Earl Carrol Vanities (tickets $3.65) and dancing at Oriole Terrace. In spite of Tom's dire predictions, his intentions were more than honorable. Two months later he gave her a diamond about the size of the twinkle in his eye, and Jenny went about in a happy trance, carefully turning her third finger, left hand, to the public gaze.

Jenny's father grumbled a little. All lawyers, he said, were nothing but hot-air artists, not that he had anything against Frank personally.

Mrs. Higgins, however, was delighted with an excuse to give a party.

It was quite a wedding.

The house—including the bathroom—was decorated with miles of white crepe paper and white tissue bells. Even the toilet-paper holder wore a huge white satin bow.

Just before the service Mrs. Higgins put some tea towels in the oven to dry out (I can't imagine why) and they caught on fire.

It caused quite a commotion. The guests got in each other's way, dribbling water and opening doors to let out the smoke. The white tissue streamers and bells swayed in the wind and rattled to the floor. It's a miracle the whole place didn't go up in flames, but fortunately there was more smoke than fire.

Mrs. Higgins had a wonderful time. She rushed about making tea, "to steady your nerves, ducky," and invited the firemen, the florist's delivery boy and a few strangers who had stopped by to see what the excitement was all about, to stay for the wedding.

"If you don't mind, old girl," Dadda said, declining the tea, "I'd just as soon have a drop of Auntie's ruin."

So Mrs. Higgins brought out the gin bottle and the wedding went merrily on.

If we had ever had any doubts whether Frank was good enough for our Jenny, we lost them now. He seemed to be having almost as good a time as Mrs. Higgins.

At the reception he talked baseball with the fire chief,

passed cakes to the ladies (though this really wasn't the responsibility of the bridegroom) and helped Dadda find his false teeth when he mislaid them. They were apt to hurt and Dadda had a trick of temporarily storing them in odd dishes around the house.

As for Jenny, the old earl would have been proud of her. Nothing that happened disturbed her gentle poise. She spoke her wedding lines in a voice so sweet and trusting that Mr. and Mrs. Wilton, who ordinarily fought like cats and dogs, held hands all through the service.

As Mother said, it was one of the nicest weddings she had ever seen.

As soon as the young couple were settled, Mother and I went over the river to call. They had bought a new house that had a pleasant smell of fresh lumber and plaster. The place was immaculate, although Jenny was still working at Frank's office.

"Don't you find it a little hard to run a house and do office work too?" Mother asked.

"Oh, no," said Jenny. "It's only until Frank gets a little better established—besides I like being able to be with him. I wouldn't want him spending all that time at the office with another girl."

Mother began to laugh. "Jenny," she said, "I thought you were the girl who was going to marry an American so he'd wait on you."

"Oh he does!" said Jenny. "He's always doing the sweetest things."

She picked up her darning. "Frank has such big feet,"

she said. Her voice was proud, as if having big feet were a special virtue which belonged only to Frank.

She thanked Mother for the tray she had given them as a wedding present.

"It's just a nice size," she said, "to give Frank his breakfast."

Mother looked startled. "Jenny," she protested, "do you mean you're giving Frank his breakfast in bed!"

Jenny blushed. "Just on Sunday morning. He works so hard, it's no trick at all for me to get the furnace going before he gets up and then fetch him a tray." She dropped the mending into her lap. "I wish I could do something really wonderful for him—not little things like polishing his shoes or bringing him a glass of water. Sometimes," she added happily, "he lets me butter his bread."

Vasiliu

The Emancipated Woman

The whole family used to feel apprehensive whenever Mother announced she was going to wash her hair. She would scan the sky with a professional gaze to see if there was enough blue to make a Dutchman's breeches, and announce that it looked like good drying weather.

This was very important. A friend of hers, Mrs. Bernard Carmichael, had had the bad fortune to have the weather change suddenly just as she was finishing her shampoo. It rained for five days steadily and poor Mrs. Carmichael went around with her hair coiled like a wet mop about her head and it developed the oddest, musty smell.

And Mrs. Carmichael's hair was quite short—only about to her waist.

Mother's dark brown hair was so long that if she scrunched down a little, she could sit on it. As a matter of fact, though, she sometimes complained, it looked more trod on than sat on. It was extremely soft and fine and for some reason (possibly because she was always in a hurry) combs and pins used to fly out from it as if drawn by mag-

nets. Every so often she had to pin up the little waterfall
that continually escaped from the bun on her neck.

The last thing she always did at night was brush it one
hundred long swooping strokes. The exercise had hardened the muscle of her right arm so that it was as firm as
that of a big-league baseball player.

Mr. Midgley, the Fuller Brush man, always gave us two
free sample brushes instead of one when he made his
rounds because Mother was such a good hairbrush customer.

"It could be worse," Mother used to say (though actually she was quite proud of her hair). "I might have been
one of the Seven Sutherland Sisters."

The Seven Sutherland Sisters, who were pictured in
advertisements for scalp products, had hair that fell to the
ground and then spread out about them like a fan.

We not only had to consider Mother's hair when the
weather was dry, we had to think about it when it was
wet. Every time it rained, we all rushed to put out the
potted begonias and place strategic pans to catch rainwater
for shampoos.

At one time we had had a large wooden rain barrel
under the eaves, but it bred mosquitoes and Mother insisted on getting rid of it. The mosquitoes never bit Father. He was never entirely convinced that they bit other
people either.

"If you'd eat your oatmeal every morning, they wouldn't
bother you," he used to say.

Mother always washed her hair right after breakfast so
as to try to get it dry by evening. The shampooing process

used an entire bottle of mulsified cocoanut shampoo, three eggs and the muscular energy of the entire family.

For some odd reason, no matter how carefully Mother planned against every eventuality, she would no more than get her head thoroughly immersed in water, than things would begin to happen.

Relatives we hadn't seen for nine years would suddenly knock at the door. The twins would fall out of trees. Their pet snakes or hamsters or the raccoon would get loose. (Some people say that raccoons are smart, but that one wasn't. It could take the ribbon off Father's typewriter, but it never could put it back.)

Once the representative of a soap company came to the door to award Mother a contest prize for completing a limerick. (Mother loved trying contests.) He made a pleasant little speech and presented a check for ten dollars while Mother dripped on the rug.

This went on for years. Mother never thought of her crowning glory as a burden. It was simply one of those things, like humid weather, head colds and frank relatives. There wasn't much you could do about it.

Then the bobbed-hair fad erupted into an explosion that lined the entire country on opposing sides of the hairbrush.

Ministers thundered against such unfeminine behavior and made dire references to Samson and Delilah, though actually it was Samson who got the haircut. Newspaper editorials blamed the crime increase and even certain economic problems on the barber's shears.

When righteous indignation failed, the opponents of bobbed hair tried real sneaky tactics. "Will Bobbing Turn

Hair Grey?" one newspaper article asked. "Will Women Go Bald?" another trumpeted, and warned of the dangers of overshampooing and too-frequent clipping. "Hair," declared a third, "was intended by nature to keep the wearer warm and to protect the head from injury." (If a bob-haired woman got hit by a falling brick and froze—serve her right.)

Defeated on these battlefields, a new strategy was tried. "The bob," one magazine warned, "doesn't go with the settled look. It is too much akin to skipping fauns."

Surely no woman who wasn't a little fast would want to look like a skipping faun. Or would she?

Eventually, the snip of shears was heard even in our conservative Canadian town.

Mother came home from a club meeting all adither. "That Allen girl over on Rosedale Avenue had her hair bobbed," she reported. "Her father locked her in her room and says he is going to keep her there until it grows out."

"There are two places where women don't belong," Father quoted grimly, "and one of them is a barbershop."

"She didn't go to a barbershop," mother protested. "She went to that new beauty parlor—André's."

Mrs. Bernard Carmichael was the first of Mother's crowd to yield to temptation. Mrs. Carmichael was the one who tried to smuggle the sugar-and-cream set across the border in her brassière.

Mr. Carmichael was fit to be tied. He said you'd never catch the Queen of England bobbing her hair and then he moved out to the chesterfield for the night, but it had a broken spring so he had to go back to the double bed. But not willingly.

Mother gave Father a tentative look. "I'm sure no one could sleep on our chesterfield. It's much too lumpy. The children never sit down. They always bounce."

"What he should have done was make *her* sleep on the chesterfield," Father said.

Mrs. J. Wilton was the next rebel. This was something of a shock as she was the sort of woman who wore stockings with lisle tops.

Mr. Wilton was so mad at her he shaved off his moustache.

"Of course, dear," Mother said to Father, "you don't have a moustache."

Father stroked his bluish chin (he always had to shave twice a day). "I wonder why he didn't let it grow into a beard instead of shaving it off. Someone in a family has to have hair."

Later that day I saw Mother looking at the beards in the family album. Some of Father's male relatives could have posed for the Seven Sutherland Brothers.

In spite of this warning, Mother cut her hair.

She didn't really mean to do it.

She had just finally succeeded in getting her hair dried. It had been an unusually trying shampoo. She brushed it out sitting in front of the dressing-table Aunt Fern had constructed out of orange crates. The crates were covered with organdy trimmed with a fringe made from those heart-shaped emery-stone pincushions. The fringe had cost more than a new dressing-table, but it was an interesting idea.

She picked up the scissors and cut a little snip off one side just to see how she would look with bobbed hair. Then she took a little off the other to even it, and then another and another. Something seemed to come over her and next thing she knew, she had cut off all her hair.

The worst of it was, she looked perfectly terrible. With a cry of anguish she stared in the mirror at the jagged edges dangling about her head. She picked her lovely lost hair up from the floor and held it about her as if hoping that by some miracle it might grow back in place.

Later she said she understood at last why sheep bleat when they are sheared. She felt just like bleating herself.

She tucked the hair like a dead body into a bag and placed it on a top shelf.

Fortunately no one recognized her on the way to the beauty parlor.

"I know I shouldn't have come without an appointment," she sobbed to André.

André ran his fingers soothingly through her uneven locks. "It is most understandable, madam, but come, come. We will turn those tears into the happiest of smiles."

He tied a pale blue drape about her plump shoulders and walked about the chair, studying her like a portrait painter.

"Obviously you are a lady," he conceded. "A lovely, gracious lady, but ah, there is so much more. We must express the real you."

Mother clutched the bib.

"We must," he decided with a magnificent gesture, "bring out the divine gamine in you."

"My husband," Mother quavered, "is a very conservative man."

"Your husband, madam," he sighed, gazing into her wide blue eyes, "is the most fortunate of men— See, we will shape the hair with the fingers. Marcels are for barbarians."

"You don't think the style is too young," asked Mother. "Do you really think I should keep it bobbed?"

"Is a woman who has known love ever willing to give it up?" André asked, raising Mother's hand to his lips and the tip to his pocket. "Bobbed hair is here to stay."

With her head feeling as light as dandelion fluff, Mother hurried home, almost afraid to look in her own mirror for fear it was all an illusion. She didn't think she had quite made the grade as a divine gamine, but the haircut was comfortable and becoming.

She took a deep breath and made a desperate decision.

No matter what Father said, she was not going to let it grow in again.

It was one of the rare occasions when Father was late to dinner. Mother kept getting more and more nervous. It was very seldom she deliberately went against his wishes.

"We're having pot roast with horse-radish sauce," she said before he even got through the door. The only thing Father liked as well as pot roast was beans baked overnight in a big crock.

"How's everything?" Father said as he kissed her. He always asked that and never waited for an answer.

He looked right at her, and he never said a word about her hair.

He ate his pot roast and buttered a scone.

Mother couldn't stand it any longer. This was worse than having him roar. He must be even madder than Mr. Carmichael or Mr. Wilton if he couldn't even trust himself to speak.

"I'm sorry, dear," she said. "I know I should have told you, but I really didn't intend to do it."

"Do what?" Father asked.

"Why, bob my hair," cried Mother. Then— "Do you mean to sit there and tell me you didn't even notice!"

Father buttered another scone. "Why, so you did. Looks nice."

Mother crumpled her Irish linen napkin and rose to her feet. "Is that all you've got to say!"

"Looks *real* nice," amended Father. Then he grinned. "I've been wondering how long it would take you to get around to it."

"Of all things!" Mother declared indignantly as she marched off to the kitchen to fetch the coffeepot. "Of all things! You might at least have pretended to be mad! Whatever will I tell the girls!"

But if Father was remiss in his masculine duty, there was at least one man who regretted Mother's shorn locks.

The next time Mr. Midgley, the Fuller Brush man, made his rounds, we only got one free sample brush.

Vasiliv.

·EIGHT·

Talent Money

That impulsive quality of Mother's was one of the things that made living with her a very interesting project. Thirty days out of the month, she behaved like a proper, middle-aged housewife. On the thirty-first she was capable of the gayest, zaniest sort of mischief imaginable. A pixie kicking off her arch supports.

That dual personality of hers cropped up in odd ways.

She wore service-weight stockings, black lace lingerie and tidy half-size dresses which always sagged a little to the rear in spite of alterations. She loved Elizabeth Browning and the goriest of mysteries. She prided herself on being a good judge of character; she liked everyone. She was recklessly generous and could never resist a bargain sale. It might not be anything she could ever use, but if it was a bargain, that was enough.

"Money," she often said, "is the root of all evil."

I don't think she referred to spending it. She always enjoyed doing that. It was keeping track of the stuff that bothered her.

Father in an optimistic moment had opened a checking account for her which chronically baffled both Mother and The Canadian Bank of Commerce. It wasn't that it didn't balance. Mother never ventured so far into the realms of finance as to attempt this. It was because people for whom Mother made out checks were always complaining bitterly that they hadn't been paid.

Father used to point out regularly that it wasn't enough just to make out a check and leave it in some pigeonhole in her desk. It must be mailed. This, Mother felt, was completely unreasonable. She had made out a check and signed her name to it. Therefore the bill was paid.

The checking account, however, was not the only source of Mother's problems. The real worry was her talent money. In June every member of the Ladies' Aid had been given a small sum which she was supposed to put to work with the hope that it would multiply like a rabbit.

In September the original capital, plus profits, was to be used for the purchase of new carpeting for the church.

The other members of the Ladies' Aid got off to a fine start. They bought boxes of Christmas cards for a dollar and sold them to Mother for a dollar and a half. They sold her doilies and aprons and jars of jelly and a long, thin, embroidered object which we discovered long after was a yardstick holder.

"I just don't like the idea of selling things to my friends," Mother complained. "Although," she added thoughtfully, "I wouldn't mind baking cakes and selling them to your father if I could ever figure out how much it costs to bake a cake in the first place."

She told her problem to Mr. Abbington, the mailman, who gave her a pair of passes to the race track to take her mind off her troubles. He couldn't use them himself because being around horses gave him asthma. He also broke out in hives when he ate lemon pie, but he was so fond of it, he ate it anyway.

As it happened, Mother had never been to the race track. The only horse with whom she was intimately acquainted was a wall-eyed mare named Josephine, who belonged to Mr. Feeney, our iceman (he also owned a crow with a split tongue who could talk). Josephine was a kindly animal who knew the ice route as well as her master, but Mother couldn't under any circumstances imagine paying good money to see her run.

However, she didn't believe in wasting anything. Mother saved the oddest things like empty nail-polish bottles and the garters off old girdles just in case they might come in handy some time.

After some hesitation she took me along too. She had a vague idea that it might not be a suitable place to take a young girl. Our Jenny, however, said that back in the Old Country, Queen Mary herself attended regular.

That settled it. If Queen Mary could go to the race track, it should be good enough for us.

From the moment she walked through the turnstile, Mother had a wonderful time. She was delighted with the bugle and the sleek horses (so different from Josephine).

She and a man with a wart on his nose and a plaid sports jacket got into quite a conversation. In this, of course, she was being inconsistent. She was always warning her daughters not to talk to strangers, particularly strange men. It had something to do with white slaves.

Our neighbor tried to explain the pari-mutuel system to Mother.

It seemed to her a very practical idea. "Do you mean," she asked, "that if I buy a ticket for two dollars, after the race they will give me a lot more money for it?"

He said it wasn't quite as simple as that and started in to explain again.

"I have a little extra money in my purse," Mother said to me suddenly. "I'm going to buy one of the tickets the gentleman is talking about."

"That Number Six horse," she said dreamily, "Johnny Jingo— I have an Uncle John. I'm sure that would be lucky."

Uncle John's last name was Stacey, not Jingo, and I doubt if anyone had ever dared call him Johnny.

"I wouldn't do it, lady," the man with the field glasses said. "That nag couldn't win if you put him on roller skates. Now you take Number Three, Boom-Boom—"

"I never did care for the shade of green his jockey is wearing," she said regretfully.

The man tried to tell her that the color had nothing to do with the way the horse ran, but arguing with Mother was like trying to make a permanent dent in a feather pillow.

She bought a ticket on Johnny Jingo, though at the last minute she almost changed her mind because the ticket taker wouldn't guarantee that he would win.

Johnny Jingo behaved very badly at the post, which pleased Mother immensely. "You can tell he has a lot of spirit," she said.

The horses were off, the field bunched like a handful of chestnuts, with one exception. Trailing blithely behind them was Johnny Jingo.

"Goodness," said Mother in a disapproving tone.

She was the sort of woman who ordinarily never raised her voice but suddenly from her throat came a clear, magnificent cry. "Come on, Johnny Jingo," she yelled. "Come on!"

Far down on the track that wound about like the ribbon on Mother's cloche, Johnny Jingo pricked up his ears. Maybe that horse had an inferiority complex. Maybe all he needed was a little encouragement. He began to move forward while Mother in the stand accompanied him in spirit by beating a bald-headed stranger with her program.

When Johnny Jingo crossed the line, winner by a nose, I personally felt the credit should have gone to Mother.

Mother looked very happy as the cashier counted out the pretty crisp green notes. "It's really honest after all," she whispered to me. "I was afraid they might try to give me a check or something useless like that."

The man who had bet on Boom-Boom tore up his ticket and his racing form. "I should spend hours figuring all the angles," he muttered. "Tell me, lady, what's good in the next?"

"I'm not going to buy any more tickets," Mother said. "There isn't any use being greedy. I'll let someone else have a chance. This time I'm just going to watch."

It was probably just as well. The jockey wearing a pretty pink shirt in the next race came in fourth.

"My horse was what they call a 'Big Shot,'" she explained to Father that night. "That's why I made so much money."

Even Father was impressed.

Mother counted out the money with an expert air. "One hundred and six dollars—the rest of the Ladies' Aid put together won't make that much. I guess that proves I have a head for business after all."

You would think after all the years he had been married Father would have gotten over being surprised at anything Mother did.

"Do you mean you gambled with your talent money!"

"Invested, Angus," Mother corrected gently. "Invested. It's really the same idea as the Christmas cards. I bought the ticket for two dollars and then sold it back to the race track people for a little more."

This logic seemed to leave Father a trifle confused, but he tried to stick to his point. "Suppose you had lost?"

Mother kissed him on the top of his head. "Now don't you worry. I'm sure the Lord will understand. Although," she admitted as she put the money into her church envelope, "I may have a little trouble with the Ladies' Aid."

NINE

Private Correspondence

There isn't anything quite like that ability of an Englishman to make his womenfolks not only wait on
him, but consider it a privilege. Canadian husbands aren't
nearly as good at it, though Father did quite well about
everything except his mail.

For some unknown reason it was impossible to convince
my mother that typewritten letters could possibly be important. She loved getting mail and she and Mr. Abbington, the mailman, were on such good terms that at
Christmastime they always exchanged cards.

Mother sympathized with him on account of his asthma
(he played the tuba in the mailcarriers' band), and the
heavy loads he had to carry.

Indeed, long before the Government got around to the
idea of carrier mail carts, Mother, who was surprisingly
practical in some ways, had tried to persuade him that it
would be simpler and more efficient to deliver the mail in
a grocery pushcart than from a sack on his shoulder.

Like most men, he had a mild crush on Mother. "Mrs.
Tippett," he would say reproachfully in his meek little

voice. "You weren't waiting for me on the porch yesterday. I was afraid you were mad at me for not bringing you a letter last Wednesday."

Mother did seem to have a feeling that if we were missed entirely on a delivery, it was because someone in the post office system had been lax on the job—not Mr. Abbington, whom she knew to be a hard-working, conscientious man, but definitely someone.

Mother enjoyed her own mail immensely and insisted on sharing it with the rest of the family.

"Imagine that," she would comment happily, "Emma Lou is going to Halifax to visit her Aunt Sweeney on her mother's side."

Nothing was more calculated to drive her into a frenzy of curiosity than not knowing all about mail belonging to the rest of the family. She would never open letters, or even read them if they were left lying about, but she was not above turning them this way and that to examine the handwriting, or even holding them up to the light.

My sisters and I loved to tease her by solemnly reading our letters and then tucking them away without a word of explanation.

Even parcels weren't safe from Mother. It took more than Do-Not-Open-Until-Christmas stickers to faze her. Long before the 24th she had opened all the out-of-town parcels (including those intended for us) and rewrapped them so neatly Santa Claus himself would have been fooled.

One year Cousin Brewster for a joke included a **very**

elegantly wrapped parcel with nothing in it except a note that said, "It isn't Christmas yet, Flora."

Mother, who opened the package on the 18th, was quite indignant at him for not trusting her.

Father's mail, however, was in a different category. It consisted entirely of business letters (Father left it to Mother to write to his relatives). Since this mail was typewritten, Mother considered it in the same class as advertising circulars and handbills and gave it equally scant respect.

In vain poor Father tried to explain the difference. Mother listened sweetly, decided it was just one of those odd masculine ideas, fixed chess tarts—his favorite dessert—for dinner, and forgot about the whole thing.

In the end Father solved the problem by putting up two mailboxes on the front porch, one labeled, "Mr. Angus Tippett" and the other, "Mrs. Angus Tippett." While this upset Mr. Abbington, the mailman, who felt it almost constituted a divorce decree, it worked out quite well. Indeed, if Father had tried the idea sooner, he wouldn't have been sued.

Father always paid his bills right on the dot, so he got quite a jolt when he was sued for $46.98 by the Merriam Furniture Company.

Father was an easygoing man, but on the few occasions when he did get angry, he made up for lost time. He phoned the company with such vehemence that Mr. Merriam himself said he would come out to the house.

By the time Mr. Merriam arrived in a Packard with a

fresh red rose in the bud vase, Father had had time to check and found that Mother had indeed bought a porch swing and canvas awnings from the company, and also that there was no record of the bill having been paid.

This didn't soothe Father at all. "Of all the crazy mutts!" he growled at Mr. Merriam. (This was the ultimate epithet in his vocabulary and we were all quite shocked.) "How do you expect to keep customers if you go around suing them instead of letting them know how much they owe you!"

"The account is six months overdue," Mr. Merriam protested. "We wrote to you three times asking for payment and never even got an answer."

"You never did anything of the sort," yelled Father, pounding the table with his fist. Suddenly he broke off and looked thoughtfully at Mother.

"Flora," he said, "by any chance did you forget to give me a letter recently?"

"I don't think so, dear," said Mother. "Let me see— There was that letter for you on your birthday from your Aunt Lucy—"

"Not Aunt Lucy," said Father. "A typewritten letter."

"I really wouldn't know," said Mother, "unless, of course, it's in the grandfather clock."

"The grandfather clock?" repeated Father.

"The sugar bowl was full," Mother said.

Father took out a little pile of unopened letters from the bottom of the grandfather clock, looked at the postmarks and sighed. There was a book-of-the-month circular, a library overdue notice, an invitation to an alumni dinner two months past, and a letter from the Merriam Company.

Father silently handed it to Mr. Merriam.

"Flora," he said, "that sugar bowl you mention, are there letters in it too?"

Inside the sugar bowl were twenty-seven cents, an ex-

pired street-car transfer, an ad for falling hair, and another letter from the Merriam Company.

"Flora," said Father, "do you have any more good safe hiding places for my mail?"

Mother thought it over. "That tall blue teapot your Aunt Hannah gave us for a wedding present, the one that always shoots over the cup when you pour."

Inside the teapot were more circulars, a recipe for bread-and-butter pickles, a bank statement, and the third letter.

"I know just how it is," said Mr. Merriam. "My wife never remembers to give me my telephone messages."

Father made out a check for $46.98. Mr. Merriam apologized and said he was sorry they had been so hasty. The two of them shook hands and said they should get together for lunch some day.

After Mr. Merriam left, Mother looked very thoughtful. "It's up to you, Angus," she said. "But I don't believe we should do any more business with people who are so careless with their records."

"Careless!" said Father, "What do you mean?"

"It wasn't three letters they sent you," Mother told him. "It was four. I just remembered that there is another under the lace runner on the buffet."

The Coffin in the Attic

Mother may have been a little absent-minded as far as mail was concerned, but we had a neighbor, Howard Elliot, who would have forgotten his head if it hadn't been screwed on tight. When he was on his honeymoon, he left his bride Evey in a restaurant and forgot all about her until a hundred miles later. Fortunately Evey was a good-natured girl and she simply ordered several pieces of apple pie à la mode and coffee and waited for him to return.

The oddest thing I have ever heard of anyone mislaying, was the coffin in our attic.

The house on the river was so large that when we first moved in we kept discovering cupboards and closets we had never noticed before.

We had been living there over a month before we knew there was a coffin in the attic.

"What a strange thing to leave behind," Mother said in a disapproving voice. "Remember Mrs. Ellery down the street who used to keep her husband's ashes in an urn over the fireplace mantel? Of course, after she remarried, it was quite awkward, so she packed them away in the basement."

"Well, all I hope," said Father, "is that no one has left a first husband here."

After some hesitation he opened the casket. Fortunately, it was unoccupied.

It was right around then that Mother noticed a small insect fluttering around and that was when she leaped to the conclusion that the casket must be infested with moths.

Now if there was one thing in the world Mother worried about, it was moths. When they were first married, moths had chewed a hole in the trouser seat of Father's good blue serge suit and she was determined nothing like that would ever happen again.

Now she went into a frenzy of action, hanging all the edible family garments out on the line to air, lining closets and drawers with newspapers and tar paper, adding a liberal sprinkling of white, peppermintlike moth balls.

Having heard that moths sometimes settled down in piano felt, though you'd wonder why with all that noise, she called in the tuner, a Mr. Twillinger.

Mr. Twillinger peered into the piano like a dentist checking back molars, twanging a wire nerve here, probing there. "Don't see none," he said.

"Please check very carefully," Mother said, and added darkly, "The coffin in the attic is full of them."

Mr. Twillinger left as soon as possible.

In the meantime Father did his best to locate the owner of the coffin. The people from whom he had bought

said it had been there when they moved in.

We didn't quite know what to do about it. It was **too** good to throw out and too awkward to give away. Besides, suppose its original owner happened to turn up.

Eventually we pushed it farther under the eaves **and** forgot all about it, except when Mother saw a moth.

Then one day, several years later, we looked out the window and saw a big man with a magnificently bald head and a black string tie walking round and round our house, checking the cement in the fireplace chimney and peering at the foundation.

Mother went to the door.

"Well, well," he said, giving her an admiring look. "I'm glad to find nice people living in my house. I'm Demery Ebehart. I built this place forty-one years ago. Thought it was time I dropped over to get my coffin."

Mother wondered if she should make him prove it was his, but he looked like a fine, honest man.

"That fool mover missed it when we left here twenty-two years ago," he said. "Good bronze casket. Got it on a bad debt from a fellow over on Gladstone who used to have a funeral home."

"Do come in," Mother said. She led him proudly into the living room with the new two-piece mohair suite with reversible cushions (we had just gotten rid of that old-fashioned black-walnut settee that had belonged to Grandmother).

Mr. Ebehart tested the living-room floor by jumping up and down. "Solid," he said with satisfaction. "Solid as the day it was laid."

On Mother's invitation he went over the whole house, clucking a little over some of the changes we had made. "See you've painted that good oak woodwork," he said. "That was fine, honest hardwood. Might as well be pine for all anyone could tell now."

"We thought the room would seem brighter with it painted white," Mother apologized.

You would have thought he was going to buy the house again. He looked at the plumbing, thumped walls and dug his penknife into a basement beam.

"I'm glad to see the place is well kept up," he said at last. "Crime the way some people let a good building run down."

We had a feeling that if the house had been neglected, he wouldn't let us live there any more.

"I built this place to last," he told us. "Not like those Cape Cod imitations some of them young squirts are putting up now. I'm seventy-five years old (he didn't look it) and I can do a better day's work than any of them. Know more than my grandsons about how to talk to a pretty woman too."

He gave Mother an unexpected nudge in the ribs.

He called in the men who were waiting outside in a pickup truck and they carried down the casket, being very careful not to mar the plaster.

Mr. Ebehart came back from the truck with a hammer in his hand. "Don't like the feel of that veranda step," he said, pounding in a few nails. He gave the house an approving farewell pat. "Don't build them like this any more," he said.

He started to get into the truck.

"Mr. Ebehart," Mother said, "why did you wait all these years to get the coffin?"

"Didn't need it," he said, and with a cheerful wave of his hand, he was gone.

Mother stared after the truck with worried blue eyes. "I wonder if I should have told him about those moths," she said.

·ELEVEN·

More Than He Could Chew

We never did find out why Mr. Ebehart wanted the coffin but we sometimes thought of it when we saw old Mr. Elliot sitting on the veranda of his niece's house. He was shriveled and brittle as overcooked breakfast bacon and even on the hottest August day, he wrapped up in a big brown blanket.

Once in a while he would call to his niece in his irritable, thin old voice, but most of the time he was silent, not answering when spoken to, either dozing or staring straight ahead with tired, empty eyes.

Then one day a most remarkable thing happened to him. He cut his third set of teeth.

As Evey, his niece, told my mother later, he started getting dreadful pains in his jaw. Poor Evey and her husband Howard were kept up night after night, putting on first hot, then cold compresses. They thought, of course, it was just his imagination when he said he was cutting teeth, but when he opened his mouth, there they were.

It caused quite a sensation. The story was in the papers and doctors and dentists came from all over to examine him. Mr. Elliot had so many visitors, some of them total strangers, that Evey had a terrible time getting her house-work done.

One man who came all the way from Guelph was some-thing of a celebrity himself. He had been born with two teeth and after they were pulled his father had had them set in a gold watch fob.

Maybe it was all the attention he was getting, or pos-sibly it was simply the result of being able to eat solid food after all those years of gumming it, but Mr. Elliot crawled out of his blankets like a butterfly shedding its cocoon.

He couldn't seem to stop eating. The nephew, Howard (he was a butcher with liver spots on his hands like cloves on a ham), brought him home the finest steaks in his shop and all the women in the neighborhood brought over pies and cakes. It's a miracle he didn't die happily of indiges-tion.

His cheeks and body began to fill out like prunes left soaking overnight, and he no longer huddled in the sun.

The biggest change, however, was in his disposition. Mat Richards who had known him when he was compara-tively young, said he had always been something of a picklepuss, but now he smiled all day long, just to show off his teeth. As teeth go, they probably weren't much. They were small and unevenly spaced (supernumerary teeth, one dentist had said), but to Mr. Elliot they were beauti-ful, and what's more, his very own.

He declined to trust them to any of those fancy modern

toothpastes and cleaned them three times a day with a mixture of charcoal and salt, being very careful not to scratch the enamel.

At first he was content just to sit on the porch and grin at people, but gradually he got up and around, shuffling slowly down the street, his hand to the small of his back.

After a while everyone in town had seen Mr. Elliot's teeth and the visitors stopped coming. One day he got an old bicycle out of the garage and rode it all the way down to the post office, turning the pedals so slowly it was a miracle the thing stayed upright.

After that, whenever the weather was good, he rode down for the mail, smiling wide and pedaling so slowly the wheels seemed to stand still. When he reached the post office he would shuffle up the steps and, still smiling, reach, reach, reach for his key and then turn it in the lock so slowly it almost had time to rust.

In a way, Mr. Elliot's downfall was probably due to his own vanity.

He entered the corn-eating contest at the United Church picnic, playing up and down on the ears like a mouth organ. He was, of course, the center of attention, showing off quite shamelessly for the benefit of some of the older ladies.

It was only after the contest that he discovered he had lost his finest front tooth—his dentist had warned him the roots were shallow.

What happened to it was a mystery on which it seemed better not to speculate.

Poor Mr. Elliot took it quite hard. Next day he failed to show up at the post office.

When winter came he went back to his blankets. Evey took her red geraniums out of the front bay and he sat there all day long. Most of the time he dozed, but if he noticed someone wave, he would smile, quite wide, so as to display the remains of his third set of teeth.

TWELVE

Deadbeat Derby

$\mathcal{M}$r. Hill, the grocer, was an apologetic little man. If you ordered anchovies and he was out of anchovies (after all, almost no one ever did buy them) he would be as upset as if he had committed a major crime and offer to have them sent out special from the city. If the weather was bad, it was his responsibility. If a previous customer had pinched a bruise on a peach (and it is amazing how many otherwise nice women do), that too was his fault.

Mr. Hill loved his store and kept it as clean as a surgeon's office, but much more appetizing. Early, early each morning he arranged his stock, as finicky as the curator of a museum, the fruit and vegetables in lovely even rows, the peaches, the German prune plums, the apples polished to mirror brightness, the grapes with their frosting of blue, the pears flat, with their stems even. He couldn't bear a gap like a missing tooth in the canned-goods section and when anything was sold, he hastened to replace it.

In many ways he was a shy man, but he was always kind to children. When we were small, he gave us a slice of bologna or an all-day sucker whenever we shopped for

Mother, though during the last years, because some of the modern young mothers objected to children being fed apart from regular mealtimes, he substituted balloons.

On Halloween night, his store was the most popular place in town. In our section of the country, instead of the children going door to door in the residential districts, we made the rounds of the stores.

Each Halloween, just as it began to grow dusk, children from all over town gathered in front of Mr. Hill's store window, jostling and shoving, trying to catch a glimpse of the candy counter, that penny heaven with its long paper strips of candy buttons, licorice whips, chocolate honeymoons and lemon drops.

"Shell out! Shell out!" we cried. "Shell out!"

The door would open, slowly, slowly, oh with such maddening slowness. Mr. Hill stood there with a basketful of small paper-wrapped bundles of candy pressed against his skinny, white-aproned figure, not saying anything, just smiling his shy smile. It was nice, fresh candy too, not the stale leftovers most stores gave.

The shouting died down and we waited, scarcely able to breathe with excitement. Then Mr. Hill would laugh and toss a handful of the little packages in the air. Instantly the pack was upon it, shouting and pushing. Another handful of candy fell like pebbles in the opposite direction. The mob broke up, then gathered again like a basket of burs. Once when our smaller twin, Duff, was knocked down in the crush, he wiped away her tears and gave her a big ten-cent box of maple buds just for herself.

Even apart from Halloween, I don't think Mr. Hill made much money from his candy department. Whenever his charge customers settled their bills, he always put a large bag of candy as a gift in with their order. This was the one thing he did that annoyed my mother. We paid cash, which meant we never got any free candy.

For years and years Mr. Hill's store was as much a part of the town as the post office. He went quietly on trying to give the town the very best in food and service. If someone wanted a jar of pickles, Mr. Hill would not only send it right over, but the delivery boy would pick up the customer's mail at the post office.

His customers continued to expect extra service and fine quality, but complained when prices were higher than the new chain store. Some of his people, like our family, paid cash, but the majority charged their bills, especially when they were a little short of money. When they had cash, they dealt at the supermarket. Since Mr. Hill was always very embarrassed at the idea of asking for payment, the bills were allowed to run on and on.

Eventually the inevitable happened. The bank gave him notice that they would have to foreclose.

Poor Mr. Hill. He had always worked too hard to have time to get married and the store was the only thing he really loved. He grew so thin his white apron dangled like an empty sack.

When he told Mother his troubles his hands were trembling so he could scarcely slice the cheese.

"Maybe if you had some kind of a contest it would help

business," Mother suggested hopefully. Mother had a tremendous amount of faith in contests and tried all of them.

"I'm afraid it's too late to start counting beans in jars now," said Mr. Hill, looking hopelessly at his account book.

Mother's blue eyes grew thoughtful. "Something on the order of a lottery," she murmured dreamily. "Put the name of everyone who owes you money in a box and then give a prize to the person whose name is drawn. It would just serve people right for not paying their bills."

All the same, it never really occurred to her that he would do it, but next day the local paper carried a most unusual announcement.

WHO IS THE TOWN'S WORST DEADBEAT?

Mr. Ellery Hill, proprietor of the Fair Deal Grocery
Store, is sponsoring a unique contest. This Saturday evening at eight o'clock, Mr. Hill will draw the name of
one of his delinquent customers, who will then be
elected Mr. or Mrs. Deadbeat of the Week. The public
are invited to guess how much Mr. (or Mrs.) Deadbeat
owes and the person coming closest to the correct amount
will be awarded a prize of ten dollars in groceries of his
own choice. In case of tie, duplicate prizes will be
awarded.

At first people thought it must be a joke. Not very
funny, but a joke. All the same, after the paper came out
a lot of people started looking through desks and saying
things like, "For heaven's sake, that can't be the right
total. I made a payment the first of last month—or maybe
it was the month before. What do you feed that bridge
club of yours anyway? Caviar?"

Next day the gold rush began.

All day long there was a steady stream of customers at
the grocery who either wanted to pay their accounts or
phoned to say that they were mailing in checks. Oddly
enough, no one wanted anyone else to see what she was
doing. Checks and money were passed as cautiously as if
they were forged.

Some people were embarrassed and some were mad and
acted as if it were all Mr. Hill's fault for letting them
charge things in the first place. All over town, orders for

cars were being cancelled, fur coats returned and an amazing number of people decided to spend nice quiet vacations at home.

Poor Mr. Hill kept looking more and more unhappy. The more receipts he made out, the larger the deposits he sent to the bank the more apologetic he became. The bags of candy he put in with the deliveries for newly paid-up customers were unusually large.

He didn't even smile when Dr. Henderson put his head in the door and asked if there was a copyright on the idea or could he try it too.

That's how it went, right up to the night of the contest.

By eight o'clock on the night of the contest, the store was packed as tight as an asparagus can. Mr. Hill had decorated the box with orange and black crepe paper left over from Halloween. The black at least was appropriate.

Mr. Hill tried to make a speech and looked very unhappy and awkward.

"It's all right," Mother said gently. "If your customers had treated you as well as you've always treated them, this contest wouldn't be necessary."

There was a minute of complete silence. Mr. Hill put his hand into the box and drew out a slip. He looked at it and turned the color of a brussels sprout. His lips moved but no sound came out.

"Draw your own name?" someone shouted.

Mr. Hill looked desperate and then his shoulders stiffened. He deliberately tore the slip in small pieces and crumpled it.

"I'm sorry it was necessary to blackmail you into paying your bills," he said quietly. "My father never did business that way. It isn't my way either. I'd like to start all over again. This is a good town and—and—"

Suddenly he looked about ready to cry.

Someone started to cheer and then everyone crowded around to shake his hand.

On Monday morning Mr. Hill opened his store up again, but with one difference. Above the cash register was a sign that said, "Please do not ask for credit. All purchases must be paid in cash."

Neither the sign nor the contest seemed to have hurt the business.

"I'm so glad everything turned out well," Mother said, shaking a package of oatmeal to try and guess if the premium dish inside was a cup. "All the same, I'm going to wonder for the rest of my life whose name you drew."

Mr. Hill smiled. "It was yours, Mrs. Tippett."

Mother dropped the oatmeal with a thud. Sometimes she was a little absent-minded about returning borrowed books but she was extremely scrupulous about money. "That's impossible! We always pay cash!"

Mr. Hill cleared his throat apologetically. "You may remember last May you had just been shopping over the river and were a little short of money—"

"But I must have paid you later—" Mother protested. Then her blue eyes widened. "I'm so ashamed. I had completely forgotten."

So Mother paid the overdue $5.62 and Mr. Hill said

he would send the groceries over right away.

"I really should have hinted that we have a bag of candy coming, just like the other charge customers," Mother said as she unpacked the bag.

As it turned out, the hint wasn't necessary. Along with our order was a lovely two-pound box of chocolates with a card marked "Compliments of Fair Deal Grocery Store."

Once again Mr. Hill had shelled out.

THIRTEEN

Happy Homicide

*I*n our family we like to date things before and after the time Mother almost witnessed a murder. "Now let me see," we will say. "That must have been just before Estelle Briggs was stabbed on our front lawn."

We do this, I think, to try to give the impression that things like that happen to us all the time. It was a high-water mark in our life and we are reluctant to concede that probably nothing like it will ever happen again.

Estelle, who was a grass widow, lived almost directly across the road from us. She was a Disgrace to the Community. Not her morals. No one even questioned them. Estelle's sins were much worse. She was a sloppy housekeeper.

It is doubtful if Estelle was as much indifferent to public opinion as she was unaware that it existed. All over town on Monday morning, sheets billowed like sails in the wind, but Estelle's always had a slightly seasick air, as if they had been flown by some shipwrecked mariner pleading for help.

There was not a yard or a house in the neighborhood as

incredibly filthy. She kept an incubator of chickens in the dining room and a squawking, reeking pen of them in her junk-littered yard. And at all times of day, mingling with the smells of rubbish which she was eternally burning, and the squawking of chickens and the bark of her dogs, came the never-ending bleat of the radio. She turned it on full each morning at six and left it until the home station signed off at midnight.

If the indignant tongues of her neighbors could have stabbed, Estelle would have met her just comeuppance long before she did.

Even gentle Young Mrs. Carter (so called at sixty to distinguish her from Old Mrs. Carter, who was eighty) spluttered like an indignant little firecracker whenever she saw Estelle. "That woman and those pesky dogs!" she would say, her small, sweet mouth drawn tight. "Just last May I had my clothesbasket on the ground while I was hanging out the wash and that yellow dog of hers deliber-ately—deliberately—" At this point in the recital, Young Mrs. Carter invariably burst into tears. "I had to boil the entire washing all over again and I still feel queer about using it," she would sob.

All day long Estelle sat alone on her cluttered front porch, a huge melted tallow of a woman with uncombed hair straggling from under a cap that looked like a soiled refrigerator-bowl cover.

Mother was fond of saying that if you can't say some-thing nice about people, you shouldn't say anything at all, but even she found it difficult to report something good about Estelle. "You must admit," she said to Father, "she gives people something in common to talk about. No one around here has to rely on the weather."

Father sniffed at the air. As usual Estelle was burning rubbish—brimstone, judging by the smell—and great black clouds of smoke were billowing over Mrs. Roger Dickensheet's terrace, where her bridge club was waist thick in chicken patties and chocolate éclairs. "It's a miracle someone doesn't try to murder that woman," he muttered.

All the same, all of us were surprised when it actually did happen.

Father was out of town on business the first part of July. At about eight o'clock on a sizzling Tuesday morning, the

rest of us were getting ready for a picnic when we heard terrific screams. We rushed outside, just in time to see Estelle running across the road towards our place, pursued by Old Dan Bing who was flourishing a pocketknife. Old Dan was the garbage man, and ordinarily a very peaceful person.

Dan cornered her beside our lawn furniture. Screaming and blubbering, Estelle collapsed into a green-striped canvas chair. Dan caught one of her arms and was preparing to slit her grimy, sluglike throat when Mother reached him.

"Give me that knife, Dan," she ordered quietly.

Old Dan was a terrifying figure towering above her,

with his dirty, tobacco-stained moustache and the coonskin cap which he wore summer and winter and in which it was generally believed he also slept.

"Give me the knife, Dan," Mother repeated.

The glare began to fade from Dan's watery, red-veined eyes. He too was one of Mother's admirers and each Christmas he searched the woods to bring her a bouquet of bright bittersweet.

"Yes, ma'am," he said meekly and handed over the weapon. Mother threw it deep into the red rambler rose-bush where it was subsequently retrieved by Wilkie Smith, the constable, who frayed both his disposition and his best pair of pants in the process.

"Sit down in that chair, Dan," Mother told him. "I want to have a little talk with you later."

At this point I was almost sorry for Dan. I knew just how he felt, with Mother's reproving blue eyes fixed on him.

Estelle moaned at the top of her lungs, while a few drops of blood trickled from one shoulder. Mother whipped off a spotless apron and stopped the flow.

"Those Red Cross classes weren't wasted after all," she told Father later. "I remembered all my pressure points. It was right on the aorta—or was it the subclavian?"

All the time Mother tended Estelle, she gently scolded Dan. "I'm really ashamed of you," she said. "What made you do such a thing?"

"She threw water on me," Dan mumbled. "Picked up a pail of water and threw it right in my face."

By this time Estelle, who had only a superficial gash, had stopped her wailing and was beginning to enjoy being the center of attention. "He spat on my sidewalk," she declared. "Him and his dirty old tobacco juice. And then he tried to murder me." She began to weep again.

"Really, Dan," Mother said, "No matter what Estelle did to you, it wasn't a very nice way to act. Don't you think you should apologize?"

There was no fierceness left in Dan. Now he was just a bewildered, rather frightened, old man, in the ragged corduroy pants that he kept up with a combination of faith and binder twine.

"I didn't mean to hurt her none, but she made me mad," he mumbled. "No female's got the right to go around cussing me and throwing water at me. I might have caught my death of cold."

Estelle glared at him. "I always said he had a mean look in his eyes, the nasty little rat."

"Dan told you he was sorry, Estelle," Mother reminded her.

Estelle subsided, but not entirely. "Spitting on my property," she snorted. "If there's one thing I can't abide, it's a man that spits."

All this time, as might be supposed, the neighbors had been gathering. Young Mrs. Carter had forgotten to put in her teeth. Mr. Roebuck, who sleeps in late, was in an old-fashioned nightshirt, split up the sides. He had been shaving and the soap still lathered one side of his ruddy face. Mrs. Roger Dickensheet wore a network of chin straps and cold cream. She stood in her doorway, clutching her hair curlers and wildly screaming, "Police! Police!"

Since our entire police force consisted of one unenthusiastic constable, this turned out to be rather futile. Eventually Mrs. Dickensheet thought the better of it and rushed inside where she could be heard shrieking, "Murder! Murder!" into the telephone.

With the aid of Mr. Roebuck, Mother succeeded in getting Estelle across the street and into her own rat's nest of a bed. When Dr. Eaton arrived a new problem arose. Estelle coyly refused to let him examine her. Maybe she was old-fashioned, she said, but she had never been treated by a doctor for anything except a cold and she just never would be able to look him in the face again.

Since Estelle was in the habit of trailing around the yard obviously clad in nothing but a cotton dress under which she bulged in an alarming fashion, this sudden attack of modesty was a little disconcerting.

Eventually she was persuaded to inch down the shoulder of her faded blue jersey nightgown, on the condition that Mother would stay close at hand as a chaperone. All during the proceedings she kept a wary eye on white-haired Dr. Eaton whose intentions she seemed to feel might at any moment become something less than honorable.

The doctor had left before Wilkie Smith, the constable, put in his appearance. Lily, the telephone operator, who knew everything that went on, had located him in the poolroom. He had a two-day beard and his uniform was rumpled, but now he made a noble attempt to show his

authority. He whipped out a little black notebook and
addressed Estelle who was propped up in bed with the
covers modestly swathed about her, because, she said, she
wasn't used to having strange men going in and out of her
bedroom as if it were a railway station.

"Did you," he demanded, "see the alleged accused strike
you with the alleged weapon?"

"Have you gone clear off your rocker, too?" Estelle demanded.

Wilkie put the book away.

Mother considered the stubble on his chin. "Don't you
think you should stop off at Ted's Barber Shop and get a
shave and a haircut?" she suggested. "You're much too
good-looking a man to go over to the county seat looking
like that."

Wilkie straightened his tie, then his shoulders slumped.
"What would I do with him while I went in a barbershop?" He pointed an indignant finger through the door
at Old Dan. Dan had taken his shoes off to ease his corns
and now he sat peacefully rocking in the kitchen, with
one of Estelle's three cats purring in his lap.

"He'd wait in the car for you—wouldn't you, Dan?"
Mother asked.

"Sure," promised Dan simply. "I ain't got no place to
go."

So it was that with his prisoner patiently sitting outside,
Wilkie not only was shaved and shorn, but had his uniform cleaned and pressed. In due course he put in his
appearance at the county seat, reeking of shaving lotion
and cleaning fluid, but looking a credit to the force.

As soon as Dan and Wilkie had left, Mother and the other women in the neighborhood got busy and gave Estelle's place a thorough housecleaning, so it would look respectable when the reporters got there.

"I don't know when anything has made me feel as righteous as scrubbing up that filthy kitchen," Mother told Father later.

Estelle bossed the job from the bedroom. As some of the women said, there isn't anyone quite as particular as a lazy housekeeper when she has someone else to do the work. "I don't believe you scalded the milk bottles," she said reproachfully, as the unwashed accumulation of years was piled in bushel baskets to be returned to the dairy. "You have to be so particular about milk bottles."

Mother found a nice pair of extra curtains at home and was busy putting them up on Estelle's front windows when Mrs. Ollie Stewart came home. Mrs. Stewart taught Sunday school at the First Presbyterian Church and she had been spending the night with her married daughter in Ridgetown. Poor Mrs. Stewart. She had lived on Lochnager Drive for thirty years and the first time something exciting happened, she missed it. She felt so bad she just sat down and cried.

It was certainly a shame and when the reporter from one of the Detroit papers came, Mother told him if he wanted to take her picture, he would have to take one of Mrs. Stewart too. After all Clara Stewart had always wanted to have her picture in the paper and it would help make up for her disappointment.

The reporter, who was a nice young fellow, looked a little dazed, as people sometimes did when they tried to follow Mother's reasoning, but he took the picture and stayed to dinner.

While all this was going on, Father was still out of town. Mother thought of trying to phone him but it wasn't as if one of our own family had been stabbed. The first Father knew about the affair was when he recognized Mother's picture on a newsstand over the heading "Principal in Murder Attempt."

He took the next train home.

He came rushing in the house next morning, shouting Mother's name at the top of his lungs.

"Are you all right?" he kept repeating. "Are you all right?"

"Of course, dear," said Mother. "I'm so sorry you missed all the excitement. I don't know when I've enjoyed myself as much."

Father was shocked. "Enjoyed yourself! A woman was almost murdered on our front lawn. You might have been killed yourself!"

"Estelle wasn't hurt very much, dear," Mother explained. "In fact, there she is now."

Coming out the Briggs front door was an imposing figure with elaborately dressed gray hair and a black-spangled evening gown whose precarious neckline was fortunately bolstered by a patchwork of bandages.

"Hell's bells!" muttered Father. Then, "Why on earth is she wearing that crazy getup?"

"It makes it a lot simpler to show visitors where she was stabbed," Mother explained. "Before, she spent too much time unbuttoning and buttoning the front of her dress. Now she just has to point."

Father gulped again. "In that creation she wouldn't have any trouble showing an appendix scar."

He started to say more, and then stopped. As if the appearance of Estelle had been a signal, the front door of both the Carter and the Dickensheet homes swung open. Young Mrs. Carter was bearing a bouquet of her treasured yellow roses. Mrs. Roger Dickensheet was carrying an angel cake. No one can make angel cake quite like Mrs. Roger Dickensheet, and she doesn't intend that they shall. Every time she gives someone the recipe, she changes it just a little.

It was obvious that Young Mrs. Carter and Mrs. Roger Dickensheet were trying to see who could reach Estelle first. Mrs. Roger Dickensheet won by a double chin. Even from that distance it was possible to see that Estelle was receiving her guests graciously, and with only a trace of condescension.

Mother watched the scene with genuine pleasure. "Estelle has had ninety-two visitors so far," she told Father. "She had them sign a guest book so she'll be able to remember to return the calls."

"Estelle," said Father, "is going to have a busy season."

Mother reached into her mending basket. "Isn't it wonderful," she said, "the way things have worked out."

Father looked again at Estelle's tidy yard and shook his

head. "There's something wrong some place," he grumbled. "It just isn't ethical— A man attempts murder, and what happens? Clara Stewart finally gets her picture in the paper—Wilkie Smith justifies his existence—the Briggs place no longer annoys the neighbors—Estelle is a social success— I tell you it just doesn't make sense."

He searched for the flaw in all this tapestry of sweetness and light and at last he found it.

"How about Dan?" he demanded. "How about poor Old Dan Bing, charged with attempted murder?"

"That," Mother beamed, "is the very best part of all. You see, Dan is getting up in years and lifting those heavy garbage cans was hard on his back. When I went to see him, he made me promise that we would all say he is a little bit feeble-minded so that he'll be sent to the county home instead of being kept in jail. That way he can be sure of a comfortable place to live without having to work. It seems he has always been a wee bit envious of a couple of his friends who are inmates there. The neighbors have been taking up a collection to buy him a present when everything is settled. Estelle gave five dollars."

"I think it's nice," said Father, "that everyone is happy."

Then Mother uttered what was, even for her, a rather remarkable piece of understatement. "It seems to me," she concluded as she finished darning the last of the stockings, "that it proves what a nice class of people we have in this neighborhood. There aren't many places where a murder would turn out so well."

Vasiliu

·FOURTEEN·

Pour on Water

We could always depend on Estelle or the Laframboise family to do something to make life interesting but I don't believe we ever had more excitement than we did the night our house caught on fire.

Early one June, we had all settled down nicely for the night, with the exception of Mother.

Mother had a theory, which seemed to work very well for her, that if she slept on a problem, it would solve itself. Before she went to sleep, she would think for ten minutes about whatever was troubling her. In the morning her mind had the answer all tied up in a neat little bundle.

On this occasion she was trying to think what to do about Cousin Harriet (she was a thirty-third cousin on the Lawton side) who had been staying with us several weeks. Harriet was a spinster with a tongue that wagged at both ends and flopped in the middle. Moreover, she was completely tactless. Father had been known to mutter that if she was born with anything in her mouth, it must have been both feet.

Short of hurting Cousin Harriet's feelings, which of course was unthinkable, there didn't seem to be any way to cut her visit short.

Mother sighed and tried to get her half of the blanket away from Father, who always wrapped them around him like a cocoon. Suddenly she smelled smoke. Mother, who had a very keen sense of smell, was always imagining she smelled something or other.

She shook my father, "Wake up, Angus!" she cried. "Wake up. The house is on fire!"

Father was a very sound sleeper, due, he claimed, to the fact that he had a clear conscience. Mother shook him again.

"Was not snoring," he grunted in an outraged tone. "Wasn't even asleep." For some reason he declined to believe that he snored and was apt to get as indignant as if accused of a moral lapse.

"The house is on fire!" Mother repeated. "Get up! Get up!"

She ran down the hall, pounding on doors and shouting, "Girls! Girls! Cousin Harriet! Wake up! Wake up! The house is on fire!"

When she heard the alarm, Cousin Harriet dangled her gray pigtails out the window shouting, "Help! Help! Save me!" until we convinced her it might be the better part of valor to use the back stairs, which seemed free from smoke, and get out of the house herself.

Lee and Duff, the twins, always practical little souls, clambered up after a suitcase in the hall closet and filled it with their favorite toys.

Bonnie clutched her diary.

Senna and I were calm, cool and collected, though afterwards neither of us was able to explain how the gold evening sandals which we owned jointly happened to be inside a pillow case in the linen closet.

Downstairs was foggy with thick black smoke.

The telephone was on the kitchen wall and Cousin Harriet rushed to it, cranking and screeching "Fire! Fire!" at the same time. Mother took it from her and told Aggie Reynolds, the night operator where the fire was.

"We've got to save things!" Cousin Harriet screeched. "We've got to save things!" She threw open a window, tossed out a vase which happened to be on the table and started for the china closet where Mother kept her Belleek tea set.

"Cousin Harriet," said Mother firmly. "Would you take

care of the children outside for me. I want to be certain
they are safe."

I herded Cousin Harriet, Lee and Duff and the suitcase
full of dolls across the yard, settled them in lawn chairs a
good distance from the house and wrapped them up in
Mother's good linen tablecloth that I had snatched from
a drawer.

"We'll be burned alive!" Cousin Harriet sobbed, completely ignoring the fact that she had reached safety.
"We'll all be burned alive!"

"I wish you'd bring me a notebook and pencil," said
Lee. "I'm going to write a composition for our class. None
of them has been burned alive."

"Later," I said, and ran back to the house.

Mother, Senna and Bonnie had filled the lemonade
pitcher, the sugar bowl and several glasses full of water
which they attempted to splash in the general direction of
the fire. The smoke seemed to be coming from the living
room and by now it was so thick we were driven back
choking and gasping. It was a relief to hear the clang of
the volunteer fire department engine in our yard.

"All those men and me looking like this," Bonnie cried.
Preferring death to dishonor, she turned and fled back up
the smoke-clogged stairs.

"Bonnie!" Mother cried. "Bonnie, come back here!"

Bonnie didn't need to have worried about the firemen.
They were a volunteer group and they were in almost as
thorough a state of dishabille as we were.

"I'm so glad you got here, Pete," Mother gasped to Dr.

Cowan. Dr. Cowan, the dentist, was fire chief and he never missed a fire. One time when the alarm rang he had a patient in the chair with some sort of plaster stuff in his mouth. By the time Dr. Cowan got back it had hardened so thoroughly he almost had to blast it out. The patient was quite annoyed, though actually Dr. Cowan was only doing his civic duty. Besides, he was so good-looking it was a pleasure to have him drill your teeth.

He ordered us back to safety, but of course we had no intention of going just when things were beginning to get interesting.

Dr. Cowan adjusted some sort of mask and groped his way into the smoky blackness of the living room. A chair went crashing.

"Are you all right, Doc?" someone kept repeating in a nervous voice. "Are you all right?"

Dr. Cowan came groping back. "Open all the windows and doors, men," he said. "All that was wrong is the fireplace damper was closed."

As if by magic the room began to clear.

"But how did the fire get lit?" Mother wondered. "We always keep it laid, but it's been too warm to use it."

Senna and I exchanged guilty glances. For several weeks we had secretly been smoking a cigarette in the living room before we went to bed. The cigarettes were tinted a pale lavender, with gold tips and scented so that they tasted like stale cologne. Their only advantage was they made us feel wild and devilish and very much women of the world.

"I don't see how you managed to get here so soon," Bonnie said from the stairway, widening her blue eyes as she looked at Dr. Cowan.

She not only had washed off the mud pack, she had unrolled the kid curlers, brushed her blond hair and changed into Mother's Christmas house coat. (Mother hardly ever wore it. She said if you were well enough to get out of bed, you were well enough to get into your clothes.)

Senna and I looked at each other. We were sooty and dirty and it would have taken more than a perfumed cigarette to make us feel glamorous.

Once in a confidential moment Dr. Cowan had told me that every time he was afraid he was falling for a girl, he tried to think about her back molars. I hoped he would remember that Bonnie had two fillings.

He didn't even seem to notice our lovely little sister. He smiled down at Mother, who in spite of the soot on her chubby face looked as fresh and sweet as white lilac. "I'd come in a hurry for your mother any time," he said.

It occurred to me that Mother had the best teeth in the family. Or maybe that wasn't the right explanation.

Shortly after the firemen had left, with a fine flourish of hats and flapping shirttails, we became aware that something was wrong with Cousin Harriet.

For one thing she hadn't said a solitary word for five minutes. She just sat on a garden bench, clutching her throat and staring pop-eyed into the air, in a manner somewhat reminiscent of our high-school dramatic society's version of *Macbeth*.

"I think she's having a fit," Lee said in an interested voice. "Maybe I could write a story about someone who had a fit."

"Asthma!" wheezed Cousin Harriet. "All that smoke brought on my asthma. I'm taking the first train home in the morning."

She sounded as outraged as if we had set the fire on purpose, whereas in reality such a simple solution hadn't even occurred to us.

"We'll take the dolls out of this suitcase if you want to use it," Lee offered before Cousin Harriet could change her mind.

We propped Cousin Harriet up in bed, gave her two aspirins and a mystery novel since she was positive she couldn't sleep, and left her wheezing bitterly and repeating that she was leaving for home on the morning train.

"If you girls must smoke, I think you should be a little more careful," Mother said as we went down the hall.

Senna and I looked at each other in dismay. So she had known all the time. Gone was the gilt and glamour, leaving nothing but the taste of stale cologne.

We went back down to the kitchen and made a pot of tea—Bonnie in particular used to drink so much tea it's a wonder she didn't swish like a washing machine when she walked. Sometimes, if we insisted, she made coffee, but it always tasted as if it had been made by someone who preferred tea.

Suddenly Duff, who was drinking a glass of milk and munching on a peanut-butter-and-tunafish sandwich (her favorite combination, though sometimes she added jam), let out a squeak. "Father!" she demanded. "Where is Father?"

The teacups clattered down. Father hadn't been with the volunteer fire department—indeed no one could remember even seeing him. "He's been burned alive," Lee wept. "My own father has been burned alive."

There was a note in her voice, however, that indicated this might make a very interesting addition to her school composition.

We ran upstairs.

There was Father rolled up in the bedclothes and peacefully snoring.

It wasn't often Mother got angry with him. Now she shook him indignantly by the shoulder. "Angus!" she cried. "Angus! Wake up! It's just a mercy you weren't burned alive. I told you the house was on fire!"

"The fire department was here," added Lee. "Everybody on the street was here!"

Father opened a reluctant gray eye. "Did they put the fire out?" he asked.

"Not because of any help they had from you," Mother said with some indignation.

"Fine," grunted Father. "Fine." And, turning over on the other side, he went back to sleep.

FIFTEEN

Call of the Wild and Woolly

*F*ather might be able to sleep through fire, storm and
blizzard, but this was in spite of the trappings of
civilization. Every so often when the west wind blew or
the wild geese honked above the river, a certain wistful
look would come into his gray eyes.

People, he said, were foolish to allow their lives to become complicated, to be nothing more than slaves to possessions and taxes (but bless his heart, he never said, or
even thought, slaves to five daughters).

He would begin to march up and down as the idea
gained momentum. "We'll sell everything we own. We'll
go to Alaska, or maybe up around James Bay, and build a
cabin in the woods—or we might get a houseboat, anchor
for a time in one place and when we are tired of it, go on
to the next place."

We children (when we were small, at least) loved these
plans and we would get out maps and plan routes and
supplies. You had to say this for Father. He might have
an itching foot, but though he longed to wander, even in
his daydreams he took along his little family.

Mother, who froze all winter in southern Ontario, and got seasick in a rowboat, never even murmured an objection to Alaska or houseboats. But that night she would have Father's favorite pot roast with horse-radish sauce for dinner (we ground our own horse-radish and it was so hot it would sear your eyeballs). Next day Father would be up to his neck in business again, the wide open spaces completely forgotten.

That was the way things jogged along for years—just one of those comfortable daydreams, like what would you do if you had a million dollars? Unfortunately, we never found out what it really would be like to have all that money, but the call of the wild—that is another story.

The oddest things sometimes stirred Father into headlong action. What happened on this occasion was that I had a boy friend named Carl who was subject to chronic nosebleeds. It wasn't anything serious, just a weak vein in one nostril that the doctor thought he would outgrow. He was a pleasant boy and very neat, except for being bumpy with handkerchiefs—used ones on the right, fresh ones on the left. The least little thing, like a sudden change in temperature or any emotion, would set his nose going. This was unfortunate because every time he tried to make a good impression on Father, his nose would bleed.

Father was a kind man, but he was exceedingly healthy and convinced that all ailments were purely imaginary (except on the rare occasions when he himself had a cold and then he had the entire family in an uproar, making hot onion poultices for his chest and changing them as soon as they turned black).

"I don't know what the world is coming to," he would mutter, looking at Carl who was stretched out on the porch glider, a bathtowel full of ice cubes dripping on the back of his neck and a nostril stuffed with cotton.

He advised Carl to eat oatmeal every morning for breakfast. Carl tried, gagging at each spoonful, but it didn't help.

As a matter of fact, it was Father's personal theory that a heaping serving of oatmeal porridge was a positive cure for anything. He himself would sit before a bowl as large as a washtub, liberally covered with brown sugar and swimming in top milk. "If a person has a good full stomach, a germ hasn't a chance to get at him," he was fond of saying. "Anyone fool enough to start the day on nothing but coffee and orange juice deserves to lose his teeth and hair." At this point he would thump his chest, modestly calling attention to the magnificent shag beneath his shirt. Indeed if it hadn't been for the conventions, Father need never have bothered about clothing at all. This hairy splendor he attributed entirely to a lifelong consumption of porridge, a benefit which we girls were inclined to view with alarm.

In time I suppose Father might have grown used to Carl, but right about then my sister Senna acquired a boy friend who played the trombone. It wasn't a real trombone, just a sort of toy that cost a dollar. Andy was quite talented and could play "It Ain't Gonna Rain No More" and "In a

Little Spanish Town" so that you could almost tell them apart.

Unfortunately, Father not only was tone-deaf—he hated music. He had a most extraordinary keen sense of hearing, and it may have been that his ear was tuned to some supersonic level. The same notes on the trombone that sent Pumpernickel, our dog, howling to his kennel, sent Father charging out to the porch. All he said was, "It's time for you girls to come in, now." But there was something in his voice so alarming that Andy jumped up, bumping his head on the hanging basket of ferns and almost swallowing the mouthpiece of his trombone, and Carl's nose spurted gore all over his new white flannels.

Father stood grimly on the porch watching them scurry down the street. "Trouble with young fellows now," he said, "is they get soft hanging around a city. You don't know what it really is to live until you sleep out in the open beneath the stars."

Senna and I were getting a little old for this kind of thing but we listened politely.

Next day Father brought home a large-size tent, an alarming kerosene stove and seven sleeping bags. He said that on the coming Saturday, we would head north.

It began to dawn on us that we were going to have to take Father and the wilderness seriously.

Before we had time to open our mouths, Mother took us firmly by the arm and led us into the next room.

"This is the first vacation your father has been willing to take in years," she said. "We'll only be away a week.

You girls are going to go and what is more, you are going to enjoy yourselves."

We might go along, but we weren't going to like it. However, we knew better than to argue with Mother. It wasn't often she put her foot down, but when she did, it was as solid as the Rock of Gibraltar.

Senna and I exchanged desperate looks.

"How about Carl?" I sniffed.

"And Andy," Senna added.

Up until then we hadn't been too impressed with the boys, but suddenly they seemed most desirable. I was two years younger than any girl in our form at school and to be quite honest about it, Carl was the only boy in it who paid much attention to me. Even a boy friend with a chronically bloody nose was better than none.

Senna and I sat on the back porch eating peanut-butter sandwiches and trying to think what we could do. We ate a whole jar of peanut butter without arriving at a solution.

At first we hoped that we might be able to persuade Father to give up the idea of the camping trip and go to our summer cottage on Lake Erie instead.

We reminded him that we could breathe lots of good pure air at the beach, and that there was a woods directly behind, full of mosquitoes and big enough to get lost in any day. But no, that wouldn't do.

It was too comfortable. It was true that we cooked on a wood stove and ate by lamplight, but we had beds. To be sure, the mattresses were about twenty years old and full of wadded lumps from being rained on when storms came up too suddenly to shutter the sleeping porch, and the nests that squirrels had built in them didn't help either, but still they were mattresses and when placed on a sagging cot, they constituted a bed.

"The whole trouble with people nowadays," Father grumbled, "is they think they have to be comfortable. Softens them up, being too comfortable."

It developed that Father had bought the tent simply to pamper his womenfolks. He himself intended to sleep on pine boughs beneath the open sky.

We spent most of Saturday morning packing and unpacking the Buick. At that time the Buick must have been about eight years old and as Father often said, good for another eight or more—he didn't approve of all that nonsense about changing models every year. He picked a good car and drove it until it was worn out.

It was a touring car with side curtains that buttoned on when it rained, and we had a little trouble stowing in an outsize tent, sleeping bags, a cookstove, groceries, luggage, seven passengers and four spare tires (it turned out that the spare tires were the most important item of all).

Father had a happy time roping luggage to the top so that the car swayed at odd angles when we rounded a curve, and tying suitcases to the running board so that it was impossible to open the door and you had to leap over it.

We were about ready to leave when Mother remembered her house plants. There was a great scurrying as we carried them over to the neighbors to be cared for, with the exception of the Jerusalem cherry which Mother had grown from a slip given her by a school friend, Myra Simpson. Mother didn't feel she could trust anyone to give it proper care, so she carried it along for the entire trip on the floorboard at her feet.

We started finally with all the neighbors running out to wave. The last we saw of our beloved home, there was Andy standing on the sidewalk, his trombone raised in the farewell sad notes of "It Ain't Gonna Rain No More" (or perhaps it was "In a Little Spanish Town") and Carl beside him with a handkerchief clutched to his nose.

About thirty miles from home Mother suddenly became convinced she had left the electricity turned on under the teakettle. Father declined to turn around but he phoned Mrs. Healy, our next-door neighbor, who promised to take the key out of the plant box and check all lights and windows.

Ordinarily Father was of the firm opinion that all other motorists were complete morons. On this day he was in a fine humor and, beyond muttering an occasional "Crazy Mutt" at some truck driver, he was at peace with the world. He even went so far as to wave a tolerant hand at another Buick, also baggage-laden, and bearing an Ohio license plate, that was coming in the opposite direction.

Even the fact that the younger children wanted to stop at five-minute intervals to go to the bathroom, get a drink or eat an ice-cream cone, bothered him not at all.

Mother worried about their eating so much cold food, but Father had thought of a solution to that problem in advance. He had invented a contraption that clamped a can of beans on the car motor. In about twenty miles or so, they were nicely warmed and we would stop (by that time we usually had a flat tire anyway), open the can of beans, divide it equally among the seven of us (we each had our own spoon and plate), re-wire another can of beans and drive on. The cans clanged a little but one more clang on the Buick wasn't even noticeable and altogether it was quite a successful experiment. Father even considered carrying the idea on a bit farther so it would percolate coffee, and putting it on the market.

Unfortunately, due to a can of beans which became overheated and exploded, it was beginning to grow dark when we reached our campsite.

We had a normal amount of trouble pitching the tent, e.g. it fell down every time we almost had it up. Father, however, was in a very happy mood and didn't get upset, even when Senna, who is left-handed, pulled the wrong rope, so that the canvas fell flapping about him like a shroud.

Eventually the tent was anchored, though goodness knows what would happen if a high wind came along. It wasn't until later we found that we had camped on a colony of ants who seemed to feel they had priority rights. We didn't move, though, because by then it had started to rain. It rained and rained without stopping, day or night.

Someone had told one of the twins that if you scratch your finger against a wet tent it will leak. So she tried it and it did and it kept right on leaking for as long as it rained.

"Just put a pan under it, dear," Mother said when we complained. From then on, the steady drip, drip mingled with the gray sound of rain beating on canvas and the chill cold wash of Georgian Bay.

Senna and I had never been so miserable in our entire lives.

The tent was too small for seven people to be very active. There was nothing to do except make occasional muddy trips to the john, which was tactfully shrouded by rain-bedraggled vines on the far side of the park. If that failed to break the monotony you could always read *The Campfire Girls at Trout Lake* which one of the twins had had the foresight to bring along.

Around about the third day Senna and I gave up even pretending to be good sports. We just crawled like fungi into our sleeping bags and wished we were dead.

Once a day we would rouse, take up a fountain pen and soggy writing paper and write letters.

We didn't actually lie—we had been too properly brought up for that—but somehow we managed to give the impression we were having a high old time. "Dear Carl"—"Dear Andy" we wrote. "There was a dance at the Casino last night." (There had been, too. We'd seen the posters.)

Around about two in the afternoon we would shiver out of the sleeping bag, put on galoshes and try to tug raincoats over the dozen layers of clothes we were wearing in a desperate attempt to keep warm. (We didn't even

take off our pajamas in the morning any more, just dressed on top of them.) We were too utterly wretched even to care how we looked.

Senna wore her glasses, though ordinarily she would almost as soon have been caught naked as wearing them on the street. Her hair hung about her neck in little damp brown strings. Mine was even worse.

Before we had left home I spent most of my allowance on a new permanent. It had cost a dollar a curl—twenty-seven dollars in all since my hair was thick. In an honest effort to give me my money's worth, the hairdresser had frizzed it right down to the roots. Now with the added effect of lake air and rain, it sprang in screen-door coils straight out from my head. It was impossible to get a hat down over it. The best I could do was rest my green straw (which also had developed an odd round protuberance in the center of the crown from the dampness) on the top of my head.

At the post office we posted our letters and collected the mail from general delivery. Carl and Andy wrote every day. It was the only thing that made life bearable. We read the letters seated in a gloomy little candy store where we were trying to make up our diet deficiency with chocolate sodas.

"Gloria Wiggins gave a party," Senna reported grimly. "Bet she couldn't wait for us to leave town to have it."

"Tina Reynolds was there," I contributed from my letter.

Tina, who planned to be a nurse, had a very professional interest in Carl and his nostril.

We ordered another soda and looked at each other in despair. Youth and love were slipping by while we wasted our lives in a sleeping bag.

All this time Father was having a wonderful time. The fish were biting in a perfect frenzy. He shipped fish back to all our old friends and neighbors and some people we hardly knew. Months later when people came into the post office with their Christmas cards, they were apt to comment that the place still smelled a little odd.

Mother, who hated rain, catching things, and boats, pinned on a gallant smile and went fishing with him. Once she accidentally caught a twenty-inch bass and Father was so proud he had it mounted for a surprise. When we returned home he hung it in the living room, where it haunted poor Mother until it fortunately got moths.

Father said that Mother was to have a vacation too, and he was going to take over the cooking. We were quite willing to let him. No one else could subdue the kerosene stove—an alarming affair that belched forth black smoke and flame and threatened to explode at any minute. The smoke Father considered in the nature of a bonus. He said it helped drive away the mosquitoes. As a matter of accuracy it just left us too wheezy to swat.

Father's menus were simple. They consisted of fried fish, oatmeal and coffee the texture of molasses, three times a day. He seemed to thrive on this diet, but Mother took to giving the rest of us vitamin pills.

We were to return home Saturday and we girls marked

off not only the days, but the hours.

That morning we awoke to a strange sensation. It had stopped raining. The soup can beneath the leak in the canvas was empty. Our younger sisters who had been more than a little underfoot all week, were gone.

As pallid as a pair of mushrooms, we poked our heads out the tent flap. Never had sunshine seemed so bright and warm. Never had the world been so beautiful.

A fresh wind was swiftly drying up the puddles. The lake gleamed like Mother's best crystal. By the time we had set the picnic table overlooking the white sand beach, we were so ravenously hungry that even oatmeal and fish tasted wonderful.

As the sun grew warmer and warmer, we began to peel off layer after layer of clammy clothing. By noon it was so pleasant we went for a swim in daring one-piece bathing suits almost down to our knees, and gave each other a shampoo. We set our hair with water-waving combs firmly clamped together, and tied a net down over the whole edifice. Lying there in the sun on blankets, we felt sanitary and comfortable for the first time in a week.

Suddenly we sat up. Until now we had had the government park all to ourselves. Now reeling along the lane was a car as baggage-burdened as our own.

"They must be nice people," said Mother thoughtfully. "It's a Packard."

"American," breathed Senna, looking at the license. Then we both dived for the tent. We had caught a glimpse of the passengers.

We took out the water-waving combs and carefully smoothed our nice sleek hair. We rubbed on round circles of orange rouge—but not too much or Mother would send us back to wash it off. We dumped things from suitcases. Finally we were elegantly attired in running shoes, gray flannel knickers, buckled at the knees like a boy's, and baggy yellow sweaters. We carefully folded identical orchid-colored scarves in triangles and tied them with the tip pointing smartly down the left shoulder.

We surveyed each other with critical approval and sauntered out.

There were two boys, about a year older than we were. Martin was six feet tall. Dennis had curly hair. They were going to go to Harvard. None of our girl friends had ever gone out with a Harvard man.

They walked with us down to the village to get the mail and ushered us into the confectionery, which suddenly seemed not only to have been redecorated but to be full of boys enviously watching our escorts (up until then Senna and I had been convinced there wasn't a male under the doddering age of thirty in town).

When we reached the park again Father had just finished reloading the Buick and was ready to start the drive back home.

Just when life was beginning to get interesting again.

"Couldn't we stay until tomorrow?" we coaxed.

Father shook his head. "I wish we could but I've got to be home by this evening for a business appointment. But don't you worry. Next year we'll take an even longer trip.

We'll start from Sault St. Marie and head north."

He beamed at Mother. "I always told you, Flora, that they'd be crazy about camping once they got used to it."

"Yes, Father," we said.

We scaled the wall of suitcases and climbed into the car. Mother anchored the Jerusalem cherry at her feet (it had grown two new berries). Martin and Dennis ran beside the car as long as we were in the park. We waved back for as long as we could see them. Just ships that had passed in the night.

"Very nice people," Mother said, "in spite of what they said about our highways." (For some reason, Canadians are supersensitive about their roads. If you do happen to hit a bad stretch of gravel or get mired, it is considered not only tactless to mention it, but it was probably your own fault in the first place.)

Our Buick, however, was made of stern stuff. We burned up the road at thirty-five miles an hour all the way back.

Eleven cans of beans later, we drove into our own street. Andy and Carl were waiting, looking as if they hadn't moved from the spot since we left.

Senna and I looked at each other. Our eyebrows telegraphed the message. Andy and Carl might never go to Harvard, but they were here, and they were ours.

We climbed out over the suitcases.

Andy raised the trumpet to his lips.

"Why Andy," Senna cried. "How wonderful! You've learned a new piece."

Carl tactfully sensed her dilemma. "It's 'Singing in the Rain,'" he said. "Andy has been practicing all week."

That Andy was certainly fonder of rain than we were.

I gave Carl my most dazzling smile. "You write wonderful letters," I said. "I think you should be a writer instead of a lawyer."

I ought to have known better.

Carl turned a happy red, then he grabbed a handkerchief and pressed it to his nose.

Father took the key out of the plant box and opened the door. "Wouldn't you think," he said in a disapproving tone, "that by this time that young man would know enough to eat oatmeal for breakfast."

SIXTEEN

Prodigal's Return

When my father's brother Ten (short for Tennyson) was about sixteen, he ran away from home. He wasn't much of a hand for writing letters, but over the years at irregular intervals Father would get a card from him simply signed with his name but bearing the most exciting postmarks—Shanghai, Brisbane, Cape Town, Buenos Aires.

No one we knew had an uncle who had traveled as extensively as this, and it made us feel quite important. On matters of foreign affairs or geography we were an authority. Our uncle had been there and we knew all about it.

We did some wonderful daydreaming over those postmarks. Some day, we said, Uncle Ten would come home, his pockets bulging with Alaskan gold and African diamonds. He would buy us little white fur coats with muffs and hats to match and we would all be rich. As we grew older, the picture changed a little. Uncle Ten, in evening clothes, would appear in a chauffeur-driven Rolls Royce, followed by a Nubian slave bearing orchid corsages with diamond clips.

Then one day we came downstairs to find a small, bald-headed man in a shabby blue serge suit, somewhat in need of cleaning, in the living room with our parents.

He seemed familiar and it was a minute before we realized the horrible truth. He looked like a cartoon of our big, handsome father.

Father looked happy and excited. "Girls," he said proudly, "this is your Uncle Ten."

We didn't even bother to glance out the window to see if the Rolls Royce was there. Only too obviously Uncle Ten was not the orchid-corsage type.

If we were disappointed in Uncle Ten, it was only too apparent that he also had some strong misgivings in connection with us. He skittered behind the safety of a wing chair, surveying us from that vantage point with as much alarm as if we had been a tribe of headhunters.

"They *all* belong to you?" he asked Father in obvious dismay.

"That's right," said Father. "Five fine girls."

"Women," said Uncle Ten, "talk too much."

For a man who had come home from his wanderings with cheap tobacco in his pouch instead of diamonds, that was no attitude to take. As soon as possible, we went back to our room.

"Whatever," said Bonnie, "are we going to tell people?"

I had been thinking about that too. I don't believe we had ever exactly lied, but somewhere along the line we had managed to give the impression that Uncle Ten was in the diplomatic service.

Senna began to hiccough as she always did when she was unhappy or ate hamburgers. "Maybe he won't stay long," she said, but we all felt that was too much to hope.

The Scotty-dog knocker on the door was tapped gently and Mother came in looking very serious. "Girls," she said, "this is important to your father. Your Uncle Ten has been very ill with some kind of jungle fever. He needs care and good food. I know you will do everything you can to make his visit pleasant."

By Father's standards there was no worse sin than failing a kinsman. Uncle Ten might not belong to the diplomatic service, but he was ours and we had better behave accordingly. As a matter of fact, we never did find out exactly what Uncle Ten was doing in so many strange places, though we did some tall speculating. We always hoped it was something a little disreputable. We had such a large supply of the other kind of relatives.

We almost killed Uncle Ten with kindness.

We stuck pillows behind his back, made him endless glasses of lemonade and did our brightest and best to entertain him.

At first we tried to draw him out about his travels, but Uncle Ten acted as if words were dangerous weapons liable to explode at any time and he used them as seldom as possible.

"Tell us about Paris," we begged.

"Noisy," he said, with an air of finality as if that covered the entire subject.

Maybe Uncle Ten didn't like to talk, but we did. We

Vasiliu

chattered to him endlessly about our boy friends, dresses and classes. If sometimes his eyes seemed a bit glazed and his attention wandered, we put it down to the fact that he had been away from civilization a long time.

We became quite fond of Uncle Ten, an affection which I am not at all certain he returned. The only member of the family to whom he ever paid any attention was Curiosity, the cat. I think he was flattered because the Persian preferred his lap and would lie there by the hour purring contentedly.

Uncle Ten was so quiet and neat, he wasn't a bit of trouble about the house. Life went on just the same as it had before.

Jenny skipped about her kitchen, singing off-key in her soft English voice and protecting the newly scrubbed virtue of the linoleum with newspapers—this was a point on which she and Mother never did agree.

Mother entertained the Philathea Class and the Women's Institute with creamed chicken patties and chocolate éclairs.

On one of these occasions poor Uncle Ten, who was attempting to slide into the house by the back way, was trapped by Mrs. Wilson. (Mrs. Wilson was a trifle deaf, but she could read lips. There was quite a bit of excitement at the Girl Guide Bazaar when she lipread what Mrs. Roger Dickensheet said about her clear across the room.)

"Do tell us about your fascinating travels, Mr. Tippett," she bellowed. "You must love the ocean."

"Get seasick," said Uncle Ten and fled, looking as if the memory were too much for him.

In spite of the fact that he was a social flop, we kept right on being kind to Uncle Ten, though he was so quiet we usually forgot he was there.

Each night we girls turned the bathroom into a dripping forest of stockings and pink panties. With seven women in the house, someone was always ironing something or washing out something. We spent hours trying out different shades of Pond's face powder (they were the most generous with free samples). We curled each other's hair with electric tongs, and singed it occasionally—if our finances were sufficiently sound, we had it done at the beauty parlor. Marcel and shampoo—fifty cents. Spanish curl—seventy-five. We made tons of fudge and sewed celluloid doll heads and ostrich feathers onto fancy silk shirred garters—sometimes since I've wondered what ever became of the fancy-garter industry. Through fudge and shampoos and laundry we talked and talked. Usually all at the same time.

Uncle Ten took to spending more and more time in his own bedroom with only the cat for company.

Then one day he came rushing down in a great state of alarm. "I think the cat is dying," he cried.

Mother took the whimpering, writhing creature from him and put it in the basket by the fireplace. "For goodness' sake," she said, "I think she's going to have kittens."

"However did that happen," Senna demanded. "We've never left her out at night."

"That," said Mother, "apparently wasn't enough."

Uncle Ten found his tongue. "You mean that creature is a female too!" he yelped, pointing an accusing finger at Curiosity. Then, "Women!" he roared in a desperate voice. "I feel as if I was living in a—a— There's just too many women in this place!"

It didn't seem a very nice attitude to take after we had been so kind to him, but we were too busy with our little expectant mother to pay any attention.

It wasn't until after Curiosity and her blind-eyed brood were comfortably settled (the Persian strain had been pepped up with some odd stripes), that we thought again of Uncle Ten.

Lee, the dark-haired twin, went to call him to dinner. She came running down with a note in her hand. "He's gone!" she cried. "Uncle Ten's gone! Do you think maybe I could write a story about an uncle who disappeared? Maybe he was murdered."

Father took the note from her.

> "Dear Angus,
> "Gone to Alaska where it's quiet.
> TEN"

"Whatever does he mean by quiet?" we puzzled.

"Poor lonely man," Mother said sadly. "Wandering homeless all over the world."

For a moment—I'm certain it wasn't more than a moment—there was an odd look in Father's eyes. "Free as a gull," he muttered. "Free as a gull."

·SEVENTEEN·

Zygeblung!

*U*ncle Ten might be the silent type, but you couldn't say the same for my mother's Cousin Brewster. Every time he visited us, we used to run around, even in July, closing the windows.

Brewster was the kind of man who would find a pearl in an oyster if he only ate them once a year, but he had one bad fault. He swore as often and as vigorously as he breathed. None of your under-the-breath profanity for him either. Even if he was only discussing the weather, you could hear him for blocks. Since we lived next door to the Anglican minister, Dr. Healy, this was somewhat embarrassing.

Mother said that what Brewster needed was a nice wife to keep him in line. Father said that nothing short of slitting his vocal cords could cure him. All the same, he was an attractive, good-natured man, and the entire family was very fond of him.

On this occasion he had brought Mother, as a gift, an Indian war bonnet. Brewster, who was a bachelor and

145

somewhat vague about styles, seemed under the impression that it was the sort of thing she might like to wear when she went shopping. Mother tried the bonnet on to please him, the gaudy feathers towering above her chubby little face.

She was still wearing it when my sister Bonnie came in, accompanied by Dr. Healy whom she had met coming up the walk. Dr. Healy, who was the soul of tact, acted as if all the ladies of his congregation were in the habit of wearing Indian headdresses around the house.

He and Brewster shook hands.

"I've never forgotten the last time I heard you, sir," Brewster said. "That was a hell of a good sermon—best damned talk I'd heard in a long time."

"Brewster," said Mother, the feathers on the war bonnet trembling with agitation. "Wouldn't you like a cup of tea?"

"I must run along," Dr. Healy murmured in a slightly shaken voice. "I just dropped in to tell you that my niece Angela will be in town tomorrow to pay us a visit."

"Such a lovely girl," Mother said. "Won't you bring her over to tea?"

After Dr. Healy had left, Mother gave Brewster a gentle scolding.

He was completely flabbergasted. "You mean I swore in front of the minister!" he roared. "Damn it, Flora, I am sorry. I try to watch my language when I visit here, but a man has to express himself somehow."

"You could say 'zygeblung!'" Mother told him firmly.

Brewster's eyebrows arched up like caterpillars. "Zygeblung?"

"If you use the proper emphasis, it means the same thing, and it sounds so much nicer," Mother said.

Brewster was so crushed that the twins offered to show him their rabbit, Rudolph, to cheer him up. However, by that time he and Father had got into a discussion about fly casting, so he said he would see Rudolph later.

As events proved, this was a mistake.

Rudolph was an extremely unusual rabbit. He was a big black buck with a fine coat, and the twins had found him nibbling on the garden hose one June morning. To their delight, they never were able to locate his owner.

They put him in the basement where he promptly chewed through the cord on the washing machine and the tires on Duff's bike. If this seems an odd dietary habit, he was also fond of lemon pie.

Nor was this the only strange thing about Rudolph. He was quite vicious. He had sharp little teeth which he was apt to use if you were careless when feeding him. The first time our iceman saw Rudolph chasing Dr. Healy's terrier down the street, he stopped drinking for a week.

In spite of his un-rabbitlike habits, the twins were very devoted to Rudolph and wanted to get him a mate, but father said No. One rabbit was a pet. Two were a menagerie.

Both Rudolph and Brewster were such rugged individualists it seems a pity they never really became friends.

Brewster did his best to escape before Dr. Healy brought his niece to tea, but Mother was firm.

Angela was a pretty, Peter Pan-collar sort of a girl who intended to be a librarian.

Brewster looked at her like Newton discovering the law of gravity and his voice seemed to petrify in his throat. He sat with a Crown Derby cup on one knee and a plate of butternut cake on the other, and never touched either, or uttered a word until Mother said she would like to send back a jar of corn relish to Angela's mother.

Brewster leaped up, splashing the tea, and volunteered to fetch it from the basement for her.

"You can't miss it," Mother called. "It's on the far side of the first hanging shelf, right beside the red currant jelly."

"Is your cousin staying long?" Angela asked after he left. She smoothed out the folds of her full skirt. "I like to wear blue," she said. "Something nice always happens when I wear blue, but I just can't stand green."

From the region of the basement came an anguished yell, the crash of glass and the sound of running feet.

Brewster charged up the stairs, his eyes wild. "I was bit by a damned rabbit," he roared, as if he couldn't quite believe his own words. "All I did was reach for a jar of corn relish and I got bit on the ankle by a rabbit."

"You shouldn't have worn gray pants," the twins said. "Rudolph doesn't like anyone who wears gray pants on account of the gas-meter man."

"Zygeblung, Brewster!" my mother kept urging. "Zygeblung!"

Brewster sat down on a kitchen chair, pulled up his trouser leg, displaying red garters and hairy shank and surveyed his wound. He said a lot of words, but none of them was the one recommended by Mother.

"Angela," said Mother, "Wouldn't you like to come out in the garden to see my Shasta daisies?"

All too late Brewster became aware of the atmosphere of disapproval that surrounded him. He pulled down his trouser leg and stood up, his face crimson. "I'm terribly sorry Angela—Dr. Healy—"

We left him still apologizing, and went out to admire the daisies.

When Angela and Dr. Healy had left we came back in the house. Brewster was seated on the couch, his head clasped in his hands.

"How could I do such a thing?" he moaned. "That girl— She's wonderful. I've been looking for someone like her all my life."

"I told you to say zygeblung," Mother reminded him severely. Then she relented. "Angela was worried for fear you might get hydrophobia or something from that bite," she said. "She offered to drive you to the doctor. She's gone over now to get her car."

Cousin Brewster soared from the chesterfield. "I thought she would never speak to me again."

"Angela," said Mother, "is a very sweet, tolerant girl— but if I were you I'd watch my vocabulary after this."

"I will," Brewster promised fervently. "I sure as hell will."

He rushed for the front door, though we noticed that

before he reached Angela and the car he had once again developed a conspicuous limp.

"I must say I'm surprised," Father admitted. "I thought Angela would be well on her way to home and safety by now."

Mother looked very pleased with the world. She dropped a kiss on the top of his head. "That proves how little you know about women. A sinner like Brewster is a real challenge to a nice girl."

None of us was very surprised when Angela (wearing

blue) and Brewster were married in Dr. Healy's garden the following September.

On that glad occasion Rudolph the rabbit was given a slice of wedding cake which he ate, silver leaves and all, with considerable enjoyment.

He then bit the bridegroom.

"Zygeblung!" groaned Brewster clasping his ankle.

"Does it hurt, darling?" wept his bride. "Does it hurt? Oh, that—that damn rabbit!"

"Zygeblung!" corrected Mother, but they were too busy to pay any attention.

EIGHTEEN

The Seamy Side of Life

After that one successful session at the race track, Mother never went back. There wasn't any reason. The horses did the same thing every day. They ran around the track.

"It must get terribly monotonous for the jockey," she said. "But I suppose they have to earn a living."

Actors have to earn a living too, but I doubt if they ever would if they had depended on Mother to support the legitimate theatre.

At that time my mother's theatregoing experience began, and indeed almost ended, with *Uncle Tom's Cabin*.

When she was about eleven a tent show came to the small Canadian town where she grew up. For weeks before the event she stared wistfully at brightly colored posters of Uncle Tom being whipped or Eliza crossing the ice pursued by dozens of bloodhounds with dripping fangs. (As a matter of fact this turned out to be a gross deception. There was only one bloodhound and he was too old and tired to have fangs.)

Admission was fifteen cents and this, frankly, was a

problem. Grandfather was of the opinion that the theatre was not only immoral, but even worse, a gross extravagance. (Grandfather was a fine man, but he could hang on to a dollar until it squeaked.)

A neighbor gave Mother a job picking strawberries at a cent a quart, provided she would promise to pick into the box instead of into her stomach.

By show time she only had thirteen cents, but the neighbor gave her two cents' pay in advance.

The tent was lit by lantern light and it had the most exciting smell—coal oil and sawdust and little boys' feet— She had a wonderful time. She cried over Uncle Tom and she cried over Eliza and the bloodhound, but most of all, she cried over Little Eva. When Little Eva died and went to Heaven she cried so hard that when her hanky got too soggy, she used the tartan skirt of her Sunday dress.

The affair would have been the high point of her existence, better even than the Kickapoo Indian Medicine Show or the Glass Blowers, if it hadn't been for a disillusioning experience. When the show was over, Little Eva came back from Heaven and stood at the exit door selling her autographed picture.

Years later Mother said she was never so shocked in her whole life. The entire affair had just been a fake. When she got home, she wept again, not for Little Eva's untimely demise, but for her even more untimely resurrection.

The cure was drastic. Mother loved to read, and she

enjoyed music, but even when she moved to the city, she seldom went to a playhouse.

It remained for my sister, Senna, and me to discover the theatre for ourselves when we were in our teens. Or rather we discovered not so much the theatre as Rollo Peters.

Mr. Peters was playing in stock with Ann Harding over in Detroit. Some people might have been taken in by her blond hair and lovely voice, but as far as we were concerned, she was just The Other Woman. We spent our good money to see Mr. Peters. We sat in the first row of the balcony, eating chocolate cherries, of which we were both passionately fond, while our hearts and digestive systems went pit-a-pat.

We never missed a Wednesday matinee.

We accomplished this by the simple expedient of going without lunch to save our school cafeteria money, and playing hooky from Windsor Collegiate Institute. We never were caught, though we had some hair-curling escapes.

Actually, the risk of being expelled was only one of the minor dangers that we faced for love of Mr. Peters.

We were not supposed to go over to Detroit alone.

Mother herself was passionately fond of Detroit and Americans, but for some reason she seemed to feel that the mere act of crossing the Canadian border was apt to put our young morals in jeopardy.

"A big city," she murmured darkly, "is no place for young girls."

It had something to do with White Slaves. She never

went into details—it is probable that her information was almost as limited as ours. At any rate, for a long time Senna and I were under the impression that if it were ever our misfortune to become White Slaves we would be kept in a house where we would have to do an inordinate amount of housework. Certainly to our minds the Fate Worse Than Death could consist of nothing more horrible than having to wash dishes three times a day.

We risked this gladly for the Wednesday matinee. We were cautious enough, however, not to speak to strange men, particularly those who looked as if they might have a sink full of dirty dishes at home.

Vasiliu

In time Rollo Peters passed from our lives, though we continued to enjoy the theatre.

We were never the type to bring out the worst in men— a fact we sometimes regretted—but eventually we knew why we were only supposed to go out with nice boys whose family we knew.

Around this time Senna and I had been left a small legacy which was simply burning holes in our pockets— neither of us had inherited Grandfather's ability to hang on to a dollar. We decided to do things up brown. We would take Mother to the theatre for a Mother's Day treat. To a road show, moreover, not stock.

Senna got tickets for *White Cargo*.

"What is it about?" I asked.

Senna didn't know. "There was the longest line at the box office," she said. "It must be good."

Mother was very pleased with the whole idea, although we were almost late because she stood at one end of Hudson's waiting room where we were to meet, and we stood at the other. We made it just before the curtain rose.

When the lovely native girl made her first slinking entrance, Mother was quite pleased.

"Except for her clothes, she reminds me of Eliza in *Uncle Tom's Cabin*," she said happily.

From then on, however, the resemblance grew fainter and fainter.

Senna and I exchanged horrified glances behind Mother's back. This obviously was no play for her.

We didn't know what to do. Mother had been brought

up carefully. She had married young. She and the Seamy Side of Life were total strangers. Innocence like hers must be protected.

At first we tried to drown out some of the more torrid lines by rustling our programs.

"Mother," we whispered to distract her. "Isn't it an interesting theatre? It's on the site of something or other. It's quite historical."

The man in front of us turned around eventually. "Would you young ladies mind displaying your knowledge another time?" he said. "I at least would rather listen to the play."

"He should be ashamed of himself," Senna muttered primly.

"Maybe Mother won't understand," I thought hopefully. "Maybe it will just go over her head." After all, it would take more than a jungle and a little heat to make Father carry on like that.

"Mother," we said desperately during intermission. "Don't you think we might as well go now? It's almost over."

"And waste part of our tickets?" Mother asked, scandalized.

When the play was over, we drew a limp sigh of relief.

"Does that girl sell her picture at the door?" Mother asked.

"No," we said. "No, she doesn't."

"I suppose," said Mother, "that things have changed since I was young."

We took her to dinner at the Book-Cadillac. Mother loved to eat out at nice places and she and the waiters always got into cozy conversations about the menu. You could be certain of a good meal and extra service when Mother was along.

"That play, Mother," I began over the soup. "I hope you weren't disappointed. We didn't know what it was like."

Mother beamed at both of us. "It was very nice of you girls to spend your money on me. Of course, I really don't think it was quite as good as *Uncle Tom's Cabin*. They could have done a lot more with that last scene."

"They could?" Senna gulped.

"When that girl—Tondeleyo—drank the poison, they should have let her die like Little Eva."

"You mean send her up to Heaven on wires?" I asked.

Mother took another spoonful of strawberry parfait. "I'm not exactly sure that was where she would have gone, but it would have made a very interesting scene."

Across the coffee cups, Senna and I exchanged uneasy glances. We must be wrong, of course, but suppose Mother *had* understood the play.

NINETEEN

Life Upon the Wicked Stage

In our most purple imaginings we never dreamed that some day we too would be connected with the theatre.

We were spending the holidays at one of the Muskoka Lakes and almost next door to us a young university group had started a summer theatre in an old barn.

Mother had never met any real actors before and she had a vague impression that they were apt to be somewhat immoral. I think it was the troupe's fondness for peanut-butter sandwiches that convinced her of their virtue. No one, she seemed to feel, could go far astray on such an innocent diet.

Father didn't think acting was immoral. He just thought it was an awful waste of time.

However, neither of them objected when Bonnie and I joined the company, for experience, not salary. Father indeed was shocked at the very idea of anyone expecting to be paid for fooling around like that.

Bonnie couldn't act at all, but she was so pretty she was tucked like a vase among the scenery whenever possible.

No one really knew if I could act or not. I was an understudy, but unfortunately our cast was healthy.

Mother took over the job of wardrobe mistress. She enjoyed backstage life immensely, though she seemed to feel that her costumes were the most important part of the play and once during a Chekhov play she reached out from the wings, to the bewilderment of the audience, to pick a bit of lint off Uncle Vanya.

We performed not only in *The Cherry Orchard,* but *Winterset, The Lower Depths* and *Ghosts.* Mother never really cared for our plays. They wouldn't have happened in the first place if people had used a little common sense, she sometimes said, and besides, there were always too many people dying.

If they had to die, it would at least be more interesting if they went up to Heaven on wires like Little Eva. Little Eva soaring gloriously across the stage was still her idea of good entertaining theatre.

It may be that the summer people agreed with her because they seemed much more interested in acquiring sunburn than culture. Each week the company floundered deeper into the red.

Karl, our director and producer, was a very sensitive young man with a pimply skin that he was trying to clear up with a combination of Freud and yeast dissolved in tomato juice.

It upset him dreadfully to have to think about money.

"You'd think we were dealing in potatoes, the way people fuss about their bills," he groaned to Mother. "You know how hard we've all worked."

Father snorted. Nothing on earth could ever convince him that acting was work.

Mother was sewing a button on the company's indispensable dress suit. This was worn by the waiters and impoverished gentlemen, of whom our plays seemed to have a generous supply. A Noel Coward hero wouldn't have been caught drowned in it.

"What we should do," Mother said, "is raise money like we do at church bazaars."

Karl stopped chewing the corner of his handkerchief. "I suppose," he offered bitterly, "that we could dress the girls up and sell oranges during intermission."

Mother thought, with some alarm, of Nell Gwynn. All that scandal, especially with a king. "What I had in mind," she said firmly, "was something more on the order of a baked-goods sale."

No one had ever gotten in trouble at a baked-goods sale.

Karl looked as if he were about to break into tears. "Crumbs and Ibsen," he moaned. (Our next play was to be *A Doll's House.*)

"Ibsen and crumbs is much better than Ibsen and bills," Mother reminded him. "Or don't you think it might be a good idea to put on a happier play for a change—like *Charley's Aunt.*"

At Karl's cry of anguish, she changed the subject. "We could sell the cakes during intermission. Most of these summer cottages have very poor cooking facilities and people get hungry for good home baking. I'll get the local women to donate the cakes and we'll charge the summer people double the usual price. That way both groups will be making a contribution."

"Couldn't you just persuade them to give us money?" Karl begged desperately. "I mean, wouldn't the ladies rather donate what making a cake would cost than go to all that work?"

"That isn't the way we women raise money, Karl," Mother explained patiently.

Next day Mother started organizing the baked-goods sale.

Karl's skin, which had just begun to clear up, broke out all over again. Someone told him to try rubbing butter on it and he went around smelling like a piece of stale toast.

If Karl was miserable, I was as happy as the grass. On the theory that nothing more could possibly go wrong (in this assumption he was quite incorrect), Karl agreed to let both Bonnie and me have a part in the new play.

He had held out against *Charley's Aunt,* but instead of *A Doll's House* we were producing *The Importance of Being Earnest.* (Mother was a little confused about Oscar Wilde. She never could understand what all the fuss was about.) Bonnie was Cecily (with a face like that no one will notice her acting, Karl said). I was Lady Bracknell (he didn't mention my face).

Life was too wonderful to waste time sleeping. We chipped dishes and dried them damply while we studied our lines.

Bonnie and I were eager students of the Stanislavski

method of acting. We spent at least half an hour a day doing our exercises—chopping imaginary wood, playing a piano, being nesting birds, bereaved mothers, thieves, a circular staircase that creaked—

"Of all the nonsense," Father growled. "Why can't they pretend to be nice healthy Canadian girls scrubbing a kitchen floor."

But Mother only smiled and sewed more buttons on costumes.

I had wonderful daydreams of the termite-ridden barn collapsing from the violence of the applause at my performance. It wasn't until opening night drew close that I began to panic. Suppose—just suppose—I wasn't quite as good as I thought. I began to think of all the dreadful things that could happen. I might freeze and forget my lines, or I might say the ones from another play—as understudy I had crammed so many roles that season. I began to get goose pimples.

The morning of the play I woke up with a magnificent case of laryngitis.

Poor Karl was almost frantic since no one else in the company knew my part.

"It's all in your subconscious," he moaned, "but we haven't time to analyze you now. What will I do! What *will* I do! We can't possibly cancel the show because we've spent the money from the advance ticket sale."

"And what about the baked-goods sale?" Mother added. "Cakes won't keep."

"Why don't you play the part, Flora?" Father suggested to Mother. "You were saying only last night that you had cued the girls so often you knew the play backwards."

If that wasn't just like Father, thinking all you had to do to play a part was know the lines. No matter how hard we had tried to explain, Mother simply didn't understand the Stanislavski method of acting. Or even any other.

Both Bonnie and I started to protest, but Karl gave her a calculating, desperate look. "Do you really know the role, Mrs. Tippett?"

After all his fine talk about upholding the traditions of the theatre, Karl was willing to throw our own mother into the hungry mouth of a theatre audience just to keep the box office open! We waited for her gently to put him in his place.

"Of course—" She hesitated. "I haven't had much experience." (This was an understatement. She had never been on a stage in her entire life.)

The horrible, the incredible truth began to dawn upon us.

Mother was stage-struck!

"You wouldn't let her, would you, Father?" I croaked.

If I had suffered at the thought of making a fool of myself in front of an audience I suffered a thousand times more in the thought that Mother might do so.

Father looked very pleased with the world. "I always thought I'd like to be married to an actress," he said.

"I could ask one of the other ladies to take care of the baked-goods sale," Mother said dreamily.

We knew when we were licked.

That evening before the performance Bonnie and I waited in the wings, clutching each other for consolation.

"I'll do everything I can to help her when we have a scene together," she promised, "and so will the other kids. If only that Mr. Sterling from the *Free Press* hadn't picked this play to review. I just couldn't bear it if he wrote something that hurt Mother's feelings."

All season long it had been our company's unsuccessful dream to lure Mr. Sterling into reviewing our plays. He used an acid-dipped typewriter, but we would have given our all for a single word of praise from him.

"It's my fault," I croaked. "Karl is probably right. I

must have some dreadful complex."

"Nonsense," said Mother, coming up behind me. "You were a croupy baby long before people ever heard of complexes—how do I look, girls?"

Most of our costumes were too small for her, but she had managed to assemble an outfit which if not exactly Victorian, was certainly interesting. It was an amazing word to apply to our chubby little mother, but she looked a trifle rakish.

"I've never seen you with lipstick on before," said Bonnie. "It looks nice."

"Prettiest girl in town," said Father. "She doesn't need lipstick."

He sounded as if he were stating a fact rather than paying a compliment.

I gulped again. If Mr. Sterling dared to say anything nasty about Mother's acting in his review, he would have to settle with Father.

"Don't be nervous, Mrs. Tippett," Karl stammered, biting his fingernails. "Whatever you do, don't get nervous."

The lights dimmed.

The first scene didn't seem to be off to too good a start. Karl took a box of aspirin from his pocket and started eating them like candy.

I waited, scarcely breathing, for Mother's entrance. She seemed to hesitate just for a moment. The baked-goods ladies gave her an enthusiastic hand, which she acknowledged with a pleased wave of her white gloves.

"Good afternoon, dear Algernon," she chirruped.

Vasiliu

I let out my breath. She was over the worst hurdle at least. She hadn't had stage fright.

I looked at the audience. Due to the presence of the baked-goods ladies and their husbands, it was much larger than usual. I hoped none of the folding canvas chairs which we used for seats would collapse, as they sometimes did.

After watching the performance a few minutes, Karl let out a sigh as if he had just taken off a tight pair of shoes.

I don't mean Mother was giving a performance that would have worried Helen Hayes. She knew her lines (and everyone else's and prompted whenever she felt it necessary). Technically, she committed every acting error in the book and yet her performance was fun to watch. Obviously she was having the time of her life. Sometimes it seemed her interpretation of the role was a little odd, but then Lady Bracknell was a somewhat odd person.

At the end of the play the baked-goods ladies and their husbands applauded with fine enthusiasm and said they had had such a lovely time and it really was quite as good as *Charley's Aunt*.

While the company were changing from their costumes, Karl and I swept the cake crumbs from the green room where the baked-goods sale had been held.

We had made enough money to pay all our bills.

"The triumph of the mass mind," Karl muttered, but he sounded bewildered rather than cynical.

Mother had changed back into her best blue silk print and white arch-support oxfords.

Karl pumped her hand. "You were wonderful, Mrs. Tippett," he said, "Just wonderful."

Father looked as if he had known it all the time, but Mother blushed with pleasure. "It wasn't at all hard," she said. "I just pretended I was Little Eva."

"Little Eva!" we cried.

"The Stanislavski method of acting," Mother explained. "I simply couldn't imagine I was Lady Bracknell, so I did Little Eva instead."

There was a long silence.

"Mrs. Tippett," Karl said when he could control his voice. "I want you to be the first to know. I've decided to take your husband's advice and go into business with my father. I don't believe I was cut out for the theatre."

"Such a nice boy," Mother said as we walked back down the cool sand beach to our cottage. "I really don't think he has an Oedipus complex or whatever he calls it. I think he just needs a good iron tonic."

When the newspaper review of the play came out, Mother was so pleased she bought a dozen copies to send to friends and relatives.

For once Mr. Sterling had tried to be kind. He said Mother had given a most unusual interpretation of the part.

But while he didn't seem to care for the play as a whole, the evening had not been an entire loss. He said he had never in his life eaten better black-walnut cake.

Vasiliu

·TWENTY·

As Young as You Feel

When our Great-grandmother Lawton was in her eighties, she was fond of saying that when she was young she had been the prettiest girl in town. "And," she would add triumphantly, "there isn't a soul left alive to prove I wasn't!"

I think we felt something the same way about our mother's athletic prowess. It was all very well for her to

say she had once held the broad running jump champion-
ship of Galt High School. We didn't doubt her word, but
it was a little hard to stretch one's imagination that far.
Mother simply wasn't constructed on jumping lines.
When I tried to conjecture how she must have looked at
the time, the best I could manage was a diminutive version
of Mother in the flowered print dress and white oxfords
she wore to club meetings, suddenly, mysteriously floating
through air.

In spite of the pictures in the family album, it was difficult to believe your parents had ever been young.

"Mother," my little sister Lee squealed one June day,
leaning over the porch rocker. "You've got some more gray
hair."

"It runs in the Lawton family," Father said comfortably,
putting down his newspaper. "Besides, I like it. Nothing
looks prettier than a young face with gray hair."

Mother wrinkled her nose. "Personally, I prefer a
young face with young hair."

Father bent to kiss her good-bye. He always kissed her
good-bye, even if he was only going to the corner grocery.
Mother watched after him a little wistfully. There wasn't
any gray in Father's hair and it was as thick and wavy as
when he was married.

The door across the street opened and our new neighbor, Mrs. Brock, came out. Mr. Brock practiced the clari-
net for an hour before breakfast every day, but we liked
his wife. She had blond, blond hair and the loveliest
clothes. She came across the street to our porch. She

didn't look quite as young close up.

"You look so comfortable in that rocking chair, Mrs. Tippett." She smiled. "You remind me of my mother."

"You must bring her over to tea some day," our mother said, but her voice sounded a little odd.

"I'd love to," Mrs. Brock answered. "I think it's so good for older people to get out once in a while and meet new people."

"Is your mother an old, old lady?" Lee asked.

"Almost fifty," sighed Mrs. Brock. "But she's really quite active. She belongs to a bridge club and does a lot of church work."

We watched Mrs. Brock hurrying back to her own home with quick, graceful steps.

"I suppose playing all that golf helps her keep her figure," Bonnie said.

"I may take it up myself," our mother remarked. "They say it's quite good exercise."

We looked at her doubtfully.

"It's a little strenuous," Senna warned. "All that walking. Why don't you play croquet or shuffleboard?"

Mother's cheeks grew a little pink. "I'm not in a wheel chair yet. After all, when I was a girl, I was quite a good athlete."

There was a tactful silence.

Lee stopped swinging the hammock. "Did you roller skate back in the olden days when you were a little girl?"

"I do wish you wouldn't sound as if I belonged in an historical museum," Mother complained. "I'm only thirty-nine."

If thirty-nine wasn't old, what was?

"It's your birthday next week," Bonnie reminded her.

"Forty, then," Mother conceded. "You'll be forty yourself some day."

That of course we didn't believe.

"Were roller skates invented then?" Lee persisted. "Did they know how to make wheels?"

"They must have gotten around to the wheel," said Mother, "because I used to play with a hoop—such a pretty red hoop with painted flowers and birds and a little red stick to roll it. I wonder why children don't play with hoops any more— We had sleds and ice skates and we played jacks quite a lot, but we didn't roller skate. If I can find a set in the stores I wonder if the girls mightn't like to play jacks instead of cards next time we meet. We all used to be quite good at it."

My mind conjured up a vision of diminutive versions of Mrs. Healy, Mrs. Bradley and Mrs. Melrose solemnly bouncing a little rubber ball and scooping up a handful of jacks on the first bounce. It must be terribly sad, I thought, to have the best part of your life all over.

"Mother," I said solemnly, "I want you to know that we will do all we can to see that your last years are happy ones."

"Why thank you dear," Mother said. "Thank you very much."

"It's odd," she added, almost to herself as she watched the twins jump over cracks as they raced down the street, "I don't feel a bit older inside than I did twenty-five years ago."

Suddenly there was a strange look in her blue eyes. "I'm tired of listening to my own obituary," she announced. "This has gone far enough. Come along, girls. I may need your help."

She picked up Lee's skates.

We followed her down to the basement. When we first moved in, we had whitewashed the walls with the idea of using it for a recreation room, but the house was so big it was never necessary. Jenny used the corner nearest the furnace for a laundry, but the rest of it stretched out in a vast expanse of uncluttered cement floor.

Mother sat down on the bottom step. "Help me put on these," she said. "I'm going to learn to roller skate."

We looked at her in horror. "Mother," we wailed. "You'll break your neck. We believe you won the broad running jump. We believe you could play golf if you wanted—only don't go trying to roller skate."

"There's nothing to it," said Mother. "It's all a matter of balance."

She tried to get to her feet and before we could grab her, she sat down hard.

"Goodness," she gasped when she regained a little breath. "I had no idea that the wheels could go in so many different directions."

We helped her to her feet. "Please, Mother," we begged. "You might break a leg."

But Mother on occasion was a stubborn woman.

She tied a pillow around her waist and put on a football helmet that Lee had secured in a trade for a doll. We tugged, pushed and steered her around the basement and didn't let her fall more than half a dozen times.

By the time she was willing to quit, we were all quite exhausted.

"When you come to think of it," she admitted, "it *is* quite a long time since I won that broad running jump."

"Would you like a game of parchesi?" Father asked that night when he came home.

Mother shook her head. "If no one minds, I think I'll just go to bed early."

"People need more sleep as they get older," Bonnie said, as she went slowly up the stairs.

We were quite relieved that Mother didn't mention roller skating again. All the same, her failure seemed to have had an unfortunate effect.

Now that we had begun to think about it, it was odd how suddenly we became conscious of Mother's age. During the next few days we noticed that even her walk seemed to have become stiff and slow and that she seemed to have gotten into the habit of putting a couple of cushions on a chair before she sat down.

We did our best to pretend that a fortieth birthday is a celebration. We bought her presents—service-weight stockings, a long-sleeved flannelette nightgown and a can of Djer-Kiss talcum (we had always loved their fairy ads). We even cooked dinner—fudge, cornstarch pudding, scorched potatoes and hamburg.

We made her rest while we cleaned the house.

"Am I tired," Lee groaned when she finished waxing the kitchen floor. "I feel eighteen years old!"

"Eighteen isn't old, silly," Senna told her indignantly.

Lee nibbled on a peanut-butter sandwich. "It is to me. You can't climb trees or run or have any fun any more. And last time Bonnie rode on a roller coaster, she got sick."

"Who wants to climb trees," I said scornfully. But all the same we looked at each other uneasily.

We all went out on the porch.

Mrs. Brock came over to wish Mother a happy birthday. "After all, as I always tell my mother, 'You're only as old as you feel.'"

"I believe you're right," said our mother.

"How nice you girls look," Mrs. Brock said. "I suppose you're all excited about the high-school prom. It doesn't seem any time since I was going to mine."

"What kind of clothes did people wear then?" Lee asked. "Did you have a hoop skirt?"

Mrs. Brock looked a trifle jolted. "A hoop skirt! Well, no. Of course my skirt was a little longer than people are wearing this year."

"Mrs. Brock," Bonnie said earnestly, "I want you to know how much we admire you. It's—honestly it's just inspiring the way you're still interested in things like swimming and dancing."

"Thanks, Bonnie," Mrs. Brock said in an odd voice. "But really, I expect to be interested in swimming and dancing for quite a long time. I'm only twenty-nine."

"I know," said Senna, "That's what makes it so wonderful—the way you still have all that energy."

"You don't have to run off so soon, do you Mrs. Brock?" Mother asked.

"I'm afraid so," Mrs. Brock answered. "I think—I think

I'll see if there isn't an old rocking chair up in the attic. I may need it sooner than I had thought."

"Whatever did she mean by that?" Bonnie brooded as we watched Mrs. Brock go slowly back across the road.

"Mother," Lee asked, "how old is old?"

Mother thought a minute. "Anyone who is ten years older than you are," she decided.

Suddenly she began to laugh. "Loan me your skates, Lee."

Father looked up from his newspaper. "Whatever are you doing with those contraptions?"

"Putting them on," said Mother. "Would you mind tightening this strap?"

"You'll fall and break your neck!" we cried in alarm. "You know what happened the last time you tried!"

"Now don't worry," Mother said gently. "I've been practising in the basement all week, hanging on to a chair. You girls meant well, but you did make me a little nervous."

"You aren't going to let her, are you, Father?" we begged.

But Father just smiled. "If your mother wants to roller skate, she'll roller skate. I'll never forget the time she won that broad running jump—"

"Mother!" we begged once more.

She got up on her feet, a little shaky at first, and then with a triumphant air, on her fortieth birthday with all the neighbors, including Mrs. Brock, running out to watch, our mother skated up and down the block, not once, but twice.

TWENTY-ONE

Anyone Can Cook

When I first started to write fiction some people acted as if they weren't quite sure it was the sort of thing that should be mentioned in public.

I remember once Aunt Lucy asked me, rather hesitantly, whatever had influenced me in that direction. I said, "Great-aunt Hannah" and she was quite shocked.

"But my dear," she told me earnestly, "Hannah was the worst housekeeper."

I suppose she was. I remember the house as being warm with love and filled with exciting treasures like sea shells in a glass bubble and a silk handkerchief with the flags of All Nations that came from the Chicago World's Fair.

Aunt Hannah hadn't been to the Fair, but her husband, Ben, went on his railroad pass. Over the years his memories had become polished with loving handling until the wonders Aunt Hannah beheld with the inner eye were even more magnificent than the reality.

Aunt Hannah was the aunt who could sing louder than anyone in the Main Street Baptist Church. She was also

the largest woman I have ever seen—she wore a man's size-ten shoe.

There was nothing Aunt Hannah enjoyed more than a thumping good cause. She had been an ardent admirer of Carry Nation and they say the mere sight of Aunt Hannah billowing around the corner was enough to clear the local saloon.

During the fight for Women's Rights, she chained herself to the voting booth, Samson with tortoise-shell hairpins, about to pull the temple down around the unbelievers' ears.

She never lost her interest in politics and every town meeting found her overflowing a front seat, knitting lace, and when necessary, putting mayor and council in their proper places.

Whenever she had a spare minute she always knitted lace. She kept ten of everything in her bureau drawers—ten nightgowns big as topsails, ten slips, ten pairs of underdrawers, all in white cotton and edged with yards of sturdy knit lace. The stuff never wore out and she tacked her surplus production onto window blinds, pillow cases and wash cloths. (Uncle Ben wore hand-tucked nightshirts with pearl buttons but he declined the knit lace.)

In addition to politics, Aunt Hannah was an active church worker, never missing a Sunday. When she wasn't outsinging the choir, she listened intently to the service, making notes on points she intended to take up with the minister later, and munching on smooth white peppermints that looked like mothballs. When my red-tasselled

Roman sandals began to beat a bored tattoo on the pew, she kept slipping me candy, so that even yet Baptists and peppermints are irrevocably mingled in my mind.

In addition to peppermints, Aunt Hannah was fond of raw cranberries, which she ate like candy. When they were in season Uncle Ben used to bring her home a bag every night as a treat. She liked to eat these when she sat up in bed to read or write—she seldom fell asleep before three or four in the morning. She wrote voluminous letters, somewhat sentimental poetry, and in her seventieth year started a mystery novel with corpses and gore on every page.

Uncle Ben was the stationmaster. He used to call Aunt Hannah "Honey-girl." In spite of the fact that she looked as if she could have outwrestled him, there was so much tenderness and pride in his voice, the term never seemed ridiculous.

He was a great hand for finding four-leaf clovers. He would walk down to the station early each morning, and by the time he arrived his fist was full of four-leaf clovers. He was always very modest about it. He said everyone had a gift for something and his just happened to be finding four-leaf clovers.

He had quite a sense of humor and was fond of playing practical jokes. I remember once when he went with Aunt Hannah to a meeting of the opposition party, he whipped out a pair of artificial ears and fastened them directly above his own. This effect, with his bald head, was somewhat like a double-handled jug. The speaker, ordinarily a man of considerable poise, paused, obviously jolted. He tried in vain to look elsewhere but his eyes kept returning in startled unbelief to Uncle Ben's head. It was quite apparent that his mind was not on his subject.

Aunt Hannah never went in for practical jokes, but it was one of the few forms of activity that she missed. At various times she studied yoga, made pierced-brass lamp shades with green bead fringes, took correspondence lessons in Spanish and won a marble-shooting tournament.

She was so busy exploring the universe that she never had time to learn how to cook.

She was undoubtedly the worst cook in town though it was not true, as some folks said, that she couldn't boil water without burning it. It was the toast that Aunt Hannah burnt. Indeed when we children were small we thought the proper method was to let it turn black and then scrape.

Actually she used the same conventional ingredients as most cooks but somewhere between the stove and table they went through a strange metamorphosis and came out tasting like something from the hardware store.

She made something called soda bread with a bitter yellow taste and a crust so tough that Uncle Ben who was no fool sharpened the knife every evening. She somehow never managed to time a meal properly, and the potatoes would be underdone while the meat was brown and brittle as November leaves. Some mornings the breakfast eggs were as hard as tennis balls and faintly green. Next morning they oozed out like mercury ointment.

Uncle Ben must have had the digestion of a billy goat. He not only ate what was put before him without complaint. He passed his plate for second helpings.

This went on for years with Uncle Ben thriving and happy on scorched cornstarch pudding and coffee the texture and flavor of crankcase oil.

Then the mayor offered a first prize of twenty-five dollars for the best cake at the town fair.

Twenty-five dollars happened to be just the sum Aunt Hannah needed to buy a new telescope—she had some interesting theories about the planetary system. Cheered on by Uncle Ben, who believed she could do anything, she decided to win the prize.

Up until then Aunt Hannah's baking had been limited to a somewhat odd concoction called "crumb cake" in which batter and raisins vied for bottom place.

Uncle Ben ordered a hundred-pound sack of White Rose flour and Aunt Hannah began the attempt to cram thirty years of cooking experience into the space of a few days.

Even Uncle Ben had a hard time saying anything kind about the first cake she baked, though perhaps that **was** because she forgot to light the oven until after the cake was in.

"Maybe," Uncle Ben said gently, "you need a different recipe."

Aunt Hannah rummaged around the string and jar tops in a kitchen drawer. "I did have a cake recipe at one time but after it got lost I just made one up out of my head."

That of course was the root of most of her cooking troubles. She not only disliked being tied to earth by anything as conventional as a recipe—she was a wild experimenter and apt to combine the oddest things together.

I think, though, she was a little embarrassed when a search of the well-crammed bookcases failed to disclose a single cookbook.

After Uncle Ben went out and bought her a good one, things went a little better, though not entirely. Aunt Hannah would dig out heaping mounds of flour or sugar with whichever cup or spoon happened to be handiest. Some of the cakes were high at one end, some in the middle and the texture varied from good to not-so-good.

Next day Uncle Ben came back from the hardware store with a standard measuring cup and spoons. Once Aunt Hannah had been persuaded to level off instead of heap, things began to progress fast.

"All it takes is careful measuring," she said in astonishment. "Now wouldn't you think someone would explain that!"

She seemed to fancy that she had made a unique discovery which cooking experts had conspired to hide from her.

Now she was willing to concede that an oven thermometer might be more accurate than thrusting a big hand inside to feel the temperature.

I suppose baking cakes is like swimming or dancing. All at once you cross over a line and you know how. All at once Aunt Hannah knew how to bake. Those big hands of hers could beat a cake into cloudlike lightness. Every cake that came from her oven was a pleasure to see and to taste.

Uncle Ben would eat a whole one all by himself and then take the rest of the day's experiments down to the depot where he was stationmaster. That week we had the best-fed engineers and conductors on the line.

As for Aunt Hannah, as always when she was interested in something, she went all the way. She tried every cake in the book.

The black-walnut cake Aunt Hannah made for the county fair was the sort of thing you dream about when you have to go on a diet. She preheated the oven, used her measuring equipment and followed the cookbook. Only once did that wild imagination get away from her. When she ran out of vanilla, she substituted wild-cherry cough syrup. Fortunately, this turned out very well, giving the cake a strange, mysterious flavor.

Uncle Ben was probably the only person in town who wasn't surprised when she won first prize. He had known she could do it all the time.

The odd part was that Aunt Hannah's newly acquired baking skill never had any effect on the rest of her cooking. Uncle Ben continued to dine cheerfully on sticky sago pudding and roasts as shriveled and leathery as a headhunter's trophy.

But when it came to cakes, there wasn't a woman in town who was her equal.

TWENTY-TWO

A Matter of Tradition

It was good luck rather than good management that we didn't have the volunteer fire department at our house every Christmas.

Christmas in our home was merry, but I won't go so far as to say it was peaceful. In the first place, the holiday season had a habit of sneaking up on us. Here it would be October and the Harvest Home Festival and Thanksgiving (we always felt a little sorry for our across-the-river Michigan neighbors who had to be thankful while shivering in late November). Next thing you knew there were Christmas cards in the mail. Mother always viewed them with as much amazement as if they had come from Mars.

Then she went into action.

She would start making lists on the backs of envelopes and assigning certain responsibilities to each of us, but someplace along the line things would happen. She would wonder if she had put orange peel on Bonnie's list, so ask Senna to get it while she was buying the parcel wrappings. Eventually we were apt to wind up with no orange peel and ten pounds of Christmas tags.

Vasiliu

Not that it really mattered. Aunt Lucy, who lived about six miles this side of Parry Sound, always sent us a fruit cake. Aunt Lucy had been a militant member of the WCTU when she was young and she wouldn't have allowed as much as a bottle of three-point-two beer in her house, but the fruitcakes were different. She made them in August, wrapped them in a soft, rum-saturated cloth and put them in an airtight metal container. From then until Christmas she resoaked the wrapping cloth every few weeks. By Christmas the smell of it alone was enough to go to your head.

For two weeks before Christmas our house looked like a rabbit warren with people popping parcel-laden in and out, closing doors and calling, "Don't you dare come in until I get this hidden!" (Somewhere around July we usually would come across a Christmas package or two that had been so thoroughly hidden it had been overlooked.)

Yet somehow in spite of all the rush and confusion, we always made it. We might have fallen arches and some of the recipients may have been a little bewildered by our gifts, but we made it. By Christmas Eve the big old house would be waxed and gleaming, smelling pleasantly of evergreen and cookies and soap. The Christmas cards had been mailed just in the nick of time, the out-of-town parcels sent special delivery. There was nothing left now except to relax and trim the Christmas tree.

Or maybe not relax.

In most families trimming the Yule tree is a period of joy and laughter. It never was in ours. Three hundred and sixty-four days of the year we were as congenial a group of sisters as you could find. Putting up a Christmas tree seemed to bring out the beast in us.

We argued bitterly over the height and thickness of the tree and where it would stand. Each of us was a rugged individualist when it came to decorations. Bonnie, who was artistic, would spend half an hour picking the perfect spot for the perfect ornament. The twins liked to toss on red and green tissue-paper chains and silver-foil stars made from smoothing out Salada Tea packages with a spoon. Each new addition to the tree was good for a ten-minute brawl.

In desperation one year, Father brought home five trees so each of us could decorate as she pleased. The living room looked like the forest primeval, and besides, arguing was half the fun.

Next year we went back to one tree.

Actually, the biggest difference of opinion as to the proper way to decorate a tree (though they were considerably less voluble about it) was between Mother and Father.

Mother, who was somewhat sentimental about tradition, always insisted on having real candles on the trees. Father, who had a more realistic nature, kept two water pails, painted red and decorated with enormous green satin bows, right beside it.

On Christmas Eve Mother liked us to gather around the tree and sing carols as she lit the candles. With the exception of Father, we made up with enthusiasm what we lacked in musical ability. He just silently clutched at the handles of the water pails.

It was a wonderful moment with the hot smoky smell of wax and the excitement of trying to watch six dozen candles all at once to be certain they didn't catch fire. (We used to divide the tree up in sections with each watcher responsible for a certain number of branches.)

As a matter of actual record, though the candle holders had belonged to Mother when she was a little girl, there had never been an accident.

Father said it was just plain fool luck, and every December he put his foot down and said No more candles.

"Of course, dear," Mother would agree. "If that's the way you want it. Only Christmas won't seem the same."

When Mother got that wistful look in her lovely blue eyes, Father was licked and he knew it. He checked his fire-insurance policies to be sure they were all in order and we went back again to the candles.

This particular year Father, as usual, had bought a tree large enough for the Elks auditorium. When he tried to bring it in from the garage, it wouldn't go through the door.

So he got his saw and began to saw and saw, making quite a litter on the veranda and breathing deep, wistful breaths.

"Just smell that resin, girls," he kept saying. "There isn't anything like it for clearing your lungs. You never hear of a woodsman who is used to sleeping on pine boughs having asthma or hay fever."

My own suspicion was that anyone who went around sleeping on pine boughs was apt to die of pneumonia and rheumatism before reaching that stage, but it was just as well not to mention such heresy.

After considerable tugging and pushing we finally succeeded in getting the tree through the door and entrance hall into the living room, shedding needles all the way. (Mother was a scrupulous housekeeper, but some of those needles were still turning up in odd spots come next Halloween.)

"The rug!" we warned. "Be careful of Mother's birthday rug."

The rug was dark blue and Mother had selected it under the delusion it would not show the dirt. Instead, it picked up lint and dog hair and at one time we had wondered whether it would be more practical to dye our wire-haired terrier to match the rug, or the rug to match the terrier. It showed every footprint too, so whenever possible we left it like an uninhabited island in the center of the room and climbed over the furniture so as not to step on it.

We spread out papers, though later we discovered that this had been all in vain and the sawdust had sifted through so that the rug looked as if it had a bad case of dandruff.

The tree was still too tall, so Father took his ax and hacked away until the living-room floor was cluttered with enough pine boughs to make beds for a dozen asthma-free woodsmen.

Eventually the tree was fastened with reasonable firmness into its holder and, for double security, anchored by

black threads to the ceiling moulding—in spite of these pre-
cautions, it was a dull Christmas season when it didn't fall
over at least once.

Now we were ready to begin the battle of the ornaments. Bonnie winced as the twins produced construction-
paper ornaments they had made at school, tarnished tinsel
strings and battered Santa Clauses.

The twins sneered at Bonnie's plea that for once we
should have a tree that wasn't icky. Friends of hers, Bonnie declared, were having a wonderful surrealist tree—bare
branches decorated with inflated rubber gloves and old
alarm clocks (actually it looked like milking time back on
the farm). Eventually Bonnie offered to compromise, a
real tree perhaps, but dusted with silver and decorated
with nothing but little pink velvet bows.

Several thousand un-Christmasy words later, the tree
was completed, with construction-paper ornaments and
pink velvet bows, blithely scrambled. It was an odd thing,
but once it was finished we were all perfectly happy with
it and convinced it was the most beautiful tree in the
world.

Now we were ready for the candles. Father growled
and opened the box. Inside, instead of the holders that
usually clamped the candles to the branches, there was a
fine string of electric tree lights.

"I thought I'd give you one of your presents a little
early," Mother told him. "It isn't fair to spoil Christmas
Eve for you every year."

Father was so touched he couldn't say a word.

He draped the lights proudly around the tree and

plugged them in. There was a loud crackle and every light in the house went out. The air filled with a hot burning smell and flames spurted along a tree branch.

"Fire!" we screamed, tumbling over each other in the dark. "Fire!"

The twins, who were very practical, began to gather up the presents in the skirts of their dresses.

Fortunately, the tree was too green to burn readily and Father soon had it extinguished.

When the lights went on again, we surveyed the damage. The tree had been knocked crooked in the confusion and the needles scorched on one branch, but that was all. We had had a narrow escape.

"We never had any trouble with the candles," Bonnie said in a shaken voice.

"I don't see how it happened," Father muttered.

Mother gave him a proud smile. "I'm certain you can fix it, Angus."

So Father did something to the floor plug and checked the tree-light wiring and tested it down in the basement.

While he was gone I refilled the water pails.

Father put the lights back on the tree. We all stopped breathing as he pushed in the plug. Blue, green, red and yellow lights blossomed in peaceful brightness.

"It's the very prettiest tree we've ever had," Mother declared, and we all agreed.

So we made a pot of coffee and put some icebox cookies in the oven. As we cleaned up the living-room rug, we all sang carols. Even Father, who had been sniffing again at Aunt Lucy's fruitcake, sang, not well, but very loud.

TWENTY-THREE

Voice in the Wilderness

My Aunt Daphne was the only one in our family who had musical talent. She used to play the piano at the Coronet Theatre during the silent-picture days. She got a dollar an evening, and improvised her own music as she went along. I saw all my first movies seated on the bench beside her. Unfortunately, I was always sent home to bed at eight-thirty, so I never knew how they turned out. There was one, I remember, called *The Unforgivable Sin* and the ad said, "God in his Heaven is merciful, but could even He forgive a sin like this?" Sometimes I brood about that one still. What *did* happen!

You couldn't exactly say that my Great-aunt Hannah had talent, but she could sing louder than anyone in the Main Street Baptist Church. She was the biggest woman I have ever seen, and when she went to church she was an impressive sight, even before she opened her mouth. She could never bear to throw out trimming and when she bought a new hat (every third year) she always added the feathers and buckles from the old ones. Over the years her hats had become an awe-inspiring collection.

When the minister gave the hymn number, he would throw a desperate glance in her direction, hoping, I think, that she wouldn't hear it. Aunt Hannah couldn't have carried a tune in a bushel basket and she never bothered over a minor detail like keeping time with the music. She just roared joyously along with choir and congregation leaping from note to note after her like nervous gazelles.

I would rather have been able to sing like Aunt Hannah than swim the English Channel.

It may have been the result of lullabies bellowed over our baby heads in a voice that would have stirred the quick and the dead, but every one of us girls was tone deaf.

In an effort to inculcate in us at least a little culture, Mother and Father bought an Edison phonograph at an auction sale. Thirty-two dollars with the records thrown in. The records were half an inch thick and the machine had an odd buzz, though Mother always claimed it had a lovely tone. (I'm not too sure about *her* musical ear either.) It achieved its purpose in that we did finally learn to distinguish between the Barcarolle and the American Eagle March, though only with difficulty.

Mother was just about willing to give up in despair when radio came into our life.

The first set we heard belonged to a neighbor named Emory Fitz. (He was a plumber and his eyes didn't match. One was blue and one was brown.)

It was a crystal set and you listened over a telephone receiver which Mr. Fitz had borrowed from a booth in the Liggett drugstore. A woman with a thin soprano voice was singing "Oh, for a Breath of the Moorlands." It was interesting of course, though not as impressive as Aunt Hannah. You didn't need a crystal set to hear her a country mile away.

Nothing would do but that Mother must have a radio. It was the beginning of a new and better world, she told Father. People three thousand miles away were now our neighbors.

Father had his doubts. In the first place he felt it was a fire hazard. That outside antenna was bound to attract lightning.

Mother bombarded him with literature about how to turn a camera or a light socket into a radio. An article in *Literary Digest* telling how two teen-age girls had made a receiving radiophone, finally changed his mind. He wasn't afraid that we girls might go ahead and make one on our own accord. It was Mother who worried him.

Mother was a frustrated mechanic.

She was the best bicycle fixer in our neighborhood and every so often a perfectly strange kid would knock on our door, wanting advice on a busted sprocket.

She was quite good at repairing things that went wrong around the house, though sometimes her methods were a little unorthodox. I remember a plumber (not Mr. Fitz; his partner) who was quite upset because she stopped a leak in the hot-water tank with chewing gum and red nail polish. He said he wouldn't have minded natural, but red was carrying it a little too far.

In spite of her mechanical ability, Mother never knew the correct names of either tools or parts. "It's a round doodad with a little squiggle at the bottom," she would explain to confused hardware clerks.

Once Father had made up his mind, he went into the business of constructing a radio with a tremendous amount of enthusiasm, ignoring the pessimistic advice of neighbors. Old Mr. Barnes, who had never forgiven the invention of the automobile, went around muttering that a fool and his money were soon parted. There was Father sinking all that money into a bunch of wires and junk and even if it ever worked (which he doubted), how did anyone know radio was here to stay?

Father spent two weeks putting together what was described in the pamphlet as a "knockout three-tube Roberts set behind a panel." He went around talking about dry cell tubes and induction coils in as profound a tone as if he had invented the entire process.

The set looked wonderful and complicated when it was completed. The only problem was, it wouldn't work.

Tearing it down was much harder than putting it together in the first place. Especially since the entire neighborhood dropped in to say I told you so.

Father was a patient man. He took it apart and put it together again, screwing and unscrewing, wiring and rewiring.

Mother stood it as long as she could. "Dear," she said, "do you think it might help if you fastened this little thingamajig to that doofunny?"

Before he could object, she took a hairpin and a pair of eyebrow tweezers from her pocket and began prodding and moving the wires about.

There was a crackling sound and music filled the air.

She gave Father a happy smile. "I knew you could do it, dear," she said.

We gathered around the radio headphones, scarcely breathing. The music would fade out, soft as mist and then just when it seemed lost forever, drift back, swelling in volume and richness until the room was full of sound.

"This," said a man's pleasant voice, "is station KDKA, Pittsburgh."

We just couldn't believe our ears. "That's where Edna Simpson moved after she married," Mother said in an awed voice. "She was that girl on Ford Boulevard who was struck by lightning in the chicken coop. I haven't seen her for twenty-five years."

With the acquisition of a radio, the whole pattern of our world changed.

Father, after a lifetime of being a firm believer in Early to Bed and Early to Rise, began to stay up half the night trying to get new stations.

Mother fell behind with her spring housecleaning as she listened entranced to lectures on how to restore suède shoes and open balky windows (you use beeswax on the pulley).

All of us spent most of our free time either listening to programs or discussing them with friends.

"Did you hear that wedding last night?" we would ask each other. "Wasn't it beautiful! The groom was so nervous."

We were careful not to be snobbish towards people who

didn't have radios, but we did feel they had never really lived.

Our local authority on radio programmes was Mrs. Meadowbrook, whose niece Eileen had sung "Would God I Were a Tender Apple Blossom" over station WLW in Cincinnati. While it was true that Eileen was a husky girl who resembled the apple barrel rather than the blossom, she had nevertheless achieved a unique honor. She was the only person we knew who had been on radio.

Of all the programs, our favorite was on our own local station, the Strolling Troubadour, Jim Ellison.

We rushed furiously through the dishes so as to be ready for his theme song, played on the guitar and sung to the tune of "Auld Lang Syne."

I don't know whether Mother got tired of hearing about Mrs. Meadowbrook's niece Eileen (Mrs. Meadowbrook would drag a conversation about dill-pickle recipes back to Eileen), or whether she had a sudden inspiration. One Saturday afternoon she took all five of us girls over to Detroit to get shoes—we wore over old ones intending to leave them there and wear the new ones back through the Customs office.

We had just finished shopping and were headed home, limping a bit and scraping our soles to wear off the obvious newness when Mother stopped suddenly.

"As long as we're over here," she said, "let's go to the radio station and tell that nice Mr. Ellison how much we enjoy his program."

If she had announced her intention of calling on the

king and queen, we couldn't have been more astounded. I'm not even sure we were convinced the Strolling Troubadour was a real person. In my mind there was a glamorous picture of someone tall, dark and debonair who came sauntering in from a castle hidden among the skyscrapers of Detroit.

"An important man like that wouldn't want to bother with us," Bonnie objected.

"Everyone likes to be appreciated," Mother said firmly. "If he's too busy to see us, we'll just leave a message with his secretary or whatever it is radio people have."

I think we expected the radio station to be guarded by Cerberus at least, but the man at the information booth told us to take the elevator to the top floor.

We got off into what looked like a dark, untidy attic with an overgrown telephone booth at one end.

A bald-headed man in shirt sleeves was balanced on a small stepladder trying to change a light bulb.

Bonnie and I leaped forward to steady the ladder as it gave a dangerous lurch.

The man climbed down and grinned at us. "Thanks, kids," he said. "I get more broken legs that way."

At the sound of that familiar voice, our mouths fell open. "You're the Strolling Troubadour," we gasped. "We never miss your program. We sent you a handkerchief on your birthday."

"I hope you don't mind," Mother said. "I'm Mrs. Tippett, and these are my girls."

The nice part about it was that he seemed genuinely

pleased to see us and glad that we liked his program. He showed us all about the station.

"Our equipment is still pretty crude," he said. "But some day we'll be one of the most important industries in the country."

Mother put down the pan of dried peas which was used

to make sound effects. "Such a lovely bunch of squiggles," she said wistfully, thinking, I imagine, what she could do to improve the station with a nail file and a pair of eyebrow tweezers.

The Strolling Troubadour glanced at the clock. "Time for me to go on," he said. "You kids know my theme song? It goes to the tune of 'Auld Lang Syne.'"

We knew the words, but we wondered if we should mention that Bonnie had been known to confuse "Auld Lang Syne" with "Pop Goes the Weasel."

"You can help me sing it," he promised.

He hustled us into the telephone booth and we all gathered around a mike on a battered kitchen table.

He nodded his head and we began to sing. At the first sound of our voices, Mr. Ellison looked a little jolted, but at least if we were weak on the music, we were strong on the lyric. With a volume and enthusiasm that would have done Great-aunt Hannah proud, we sang

> Mother Miller's Delicatessen Shop
> Is the only store for me,
> Dill pickles, salami, Limburg too,
> The finest quality.

At long last we too were on radio. Let Mrs. Meadowbrook's niece Eileen top that with an apple blossom.

·TWENTY-FOUR·

The Inventor's Wife

My sisters and I might be deficient in musical talent but that undoubtedly was because our proper field was the drama. At one time I took elocution lessons from a Miss Norris who lived on Devonshire Road. The elocution lessons were supposed to equip me with social poise but while they failed utterly of their object, they did furnish me with one missile. Given the slightest encouragement (or even without it) I would deliver with the utmost eloquence a piece called "The Inventor's Wife."

At that time neither Miss Norris nor I had ever heard of the Stanislavski method of acting, but he would have been proud of me. I *was* the bed that got up and shook itself. I *was* the cradle that rocked too hard and threw the baby out on the floor. (Sometimes since I've thought about that baby and wondered if he grew up to be an inventor, too.)

But my big scene, the real heartthrob of the entire piece, came when I held my hands out simply to the audience and said in brave accents,

> If you think you are sick of your life
> Just come and change places with me for a spell
> For I'm an inventor's wife.

That really got them. The Women's Institute must have heard the recitation a dozen times, but they still applauded.

Ordinarily a piece like that would carry a person through her entire social life, but I was unfortunate. My father's sister Daphne married a real inventor. In the interests of tact, "The Inventor's Wife" was dropped from my repertory and Joaquin Miller's "Columbus" substituted. I put my all into "Sail on! Sail on! Sail on! And on!" but it didn't get the same results.

Aunt Daphne's new husband, Stanley, was an Englishman with the most charming manners. (A remittance man, some people said.) He was also a genius, so Aunt Daphne claimed, and since he seemed to be able to live without working, we were inclined to believe her. Sometimes he would disappear down into his basement work-shop, but generally he spent his time slumped in a comfortable chair, staring into the fireplace in bad weather, or seated in his garden if it was good, thinking up ideas.

This caused a good deal of talk among the neighbors. Some people thought it was almost immoral for anyone to be so comfortable when he was working, but Aunt Daphne used to tiptoe around and if any of us became too noisy while visiting, she would speak very firmly.

It was while he was in the garden following a long rainy spring, that Uncle Stanley conceived a most interesting theory for solving the world's economic troubles. It was so simple, you would wonder why no one had ever thought of it before. If people could learn to eat grass, they wouldn't have to waste money on groceries.

For a time Uncle Stanley considered keeping this mag-nificent discovery to himself—at least until he had ob-tained a patent—then he generously decided to share it with the world. Whenever possible he gave little lectures.

This involved considerable sacrifice on his part for in spite of his charm, he was a very nervous public speaker.

In an effort to help him my father suggested that he might feel a little less self-conscious if he would only con-sider how ridiculous his audience would look without their clothes.

For a while after that Uncle Stanley mentally undressed his listeners one by one and really did much better—it was, he felt, quite an interesting experiment.

Then one day while he was lecturing to the Women's

Institute he had a dreadful thought. Suppose his audience was doing the same thing to him.

Hurriedly he mentally returned several half-size flowered prints to their rightful owners and concluded the speech in an almost total state of collapse.

The ladies were very nice about the idea of eating grass, but they continued to serve their usual club luncheons of creamed chicken and chocolate-cocoanut Bavarian pie.

In spite of these discouragements, Uncle Stanley kept a stiff upper lip. Every time he cut the lawn, he brought a great pile of grass into the house, washed it carefully in the colander and put it on to boil. He had a great deal of imagination and he tried the grass out in every possible way. I remember one time he served it with cream sauce. The leftovers (e.g. all of it but one spoonful) he rolled in cracker crumbs and fried in deep fat. He tried to make grass into soup, he served it chilled as a salad with mayonnaise and even stirred it into a cake mixture. Apart from their ingenuity, the recipes had one thing in common. They were completely inedible.

Like Christopher Columbus, Uncle Stanley sailed right on and on, cooking bushel after bushel of grass, trying it fried, boiled and baked.

Owing to a sinus condition, Uncle Stanley's sense of taste was somewhat deficient, so he felt that his wife should be willing to help him by acting as a guinea pig. Poor Aunt Daphne was fond of food and for once her faith in her husband seemed to falter.

"The trouble with Englishmen is they expect too much

of a wife," she wept. "No woman should be asked to live on rabbit food."

"Now where would Thomas Edison be if his wife had taken that attitude?" my father teased.

"You needn't tell me he ever asked his wife to eat electric-light bulbs," Aunt Daphne declared and began to weep again.

It is quite possible that their marriage might have gone completely on the rocks if around about this time Uncle Stanley hadn't become acquainted with a Mr. Throndyke. They met when they accidentally collided outside a health-food shop where Mr. Throndyke had just purchased his month's supply of wheat germ.

Mr. Throndyke was both sympathetic and intelligent. He felt that Uncle Stanley's theory of feeding the world on grass was not only reasonable but proper. He went farther than that. He volunteered to try the diet himself.

Uncle Stanley was deeply touched. He took Mr. Throndyke home with him. With his own hands he mowed a shady strip on the west side of the lawn, where he personally felt the grass was unusually choice. As quickly as possible (for to a genuine connoisseur even a brief delay would be detrimental to the flavor) he plunged the grass into a small amount of boiling water, reduced it to a sodden mass and served it liberally dosed with best creamery butter.

Mr. Throndyke took some of the mixture on his fork. It was an intense moment. Mr. Throndyke took a second nibble and Uncle Stanley was almost beside himself with

pleasure. This was the first, the very first time anyone had
gone beyond a gagging first swallow. Mr. Throndyke took
another and another. The grass, he said, had something of
the flavor of spinach, with a dash—just a dash—of brussels
sprouts.

It seems ironic that with success so close, the accident
occurred. It may be that in his eagerness Uncle Stanley
had not cooked the grass sufficiently, for apparently a
blade lodged in Mr. Throndyke's throat. His face turned
a deep purple and he lurched to his feet, clutching the air
and uttering strange, gasping sounds.

Always resourceful, Uncle Stanley upended Mr. Throndyke over the arm of a Cape Cod garden chair and
thumped him vigorously on the back, emptying his pockets
of spare change, a fountain pen and several business cards,
but also dislodging the grass.

Mr. Throndyke recovered his breath, his valuables and
unfortunately, his voice. In a tone that brought neighbors
for a block around out on their porches, he accused Uncle
Stanley of deliberately trying to assassinate him and concluded with the information, shouted from the middle of
the street, that he was on his way to see his lawyer.

He was as good as his word.

The matter was settled out of court but the whole affair
upset Uncle Stanley so that he took to his bed. The doctor after talking to Aunt Daphne put him on a high-pro-
tein diet, consisting chiefly of steak. For days Uncle
Stanley lay there, nibbling sadly on porterhouse. By the
time he had recovered, it was autumn and the grass turn-

ing too brown to be edible.

During the winter Uncle Stanley became engrossed in the problem of how to run automobiles on energy derived from the sun—his difficulty was that the motor would stop every time the sun went behind a cloud.

Once he was heard to say that he didn't believe the world was ready yet for grass.

However, rather than take any chances, almost before the frost was out of the ground next spring, Aunt Daphne had the entire lawn spaded and turned into a concrete terrace which she painted green.

As for Mr. Throndyke, fortunately no one ever saw him again.

TWENTY-FIVE

No Trouble At All

Aunt Daphne had a very bad habit of trying to do two
things at a time.

Every Monday morning she would start the hot water
running into the washing machine and then hurry upstairs
to prepare breakfast for her husband, Stanley. Invariably
when she returned, the machine had overflowed and the
laundry room was inch deep in water. By the time she finished cleaning up that mess, the coffee would have boiled
over and the toast charred.

When she canned, she also cleaned cupboards and
washed woodwork. One year she overheated the paraffin
for the crabapple jelly so that it exploded all over the
kitchen ceiling and it was only a mercy the house didn't
burn down.

But even she should have known better than to try to
mix a cake and take a bath at the same time.

Uncle Stanley had phoned at four-thirty in the afternoon to say he was bringing home to dinner a man who
might invest in one of his inventions, an electric corn-
parer and bunion-remover.

Aunt Daphne didn't like unexpected guests.

Before she invited anyone over she always gave the house a thorough cleaning, including the clothes closets and the attic because you never could tell but what Stanley might decide to take someone through them.

Once, several years before, some people named Smith whom they had met while on vacation at Lake Louise, had dropped in unannounced. Nothing would do but that Stanley had to show them all over the house. Aunt Daphne had spent the entire morning ironing (Uncle Stanley always wore a clean white shirt every day) and for perhaps the first time in her life she hadn't made the bed.

She had managed to get upstairs first and close the door, but in spite of her frantic signals, Stanley had opened it and taken the Smiths right in. She was so embarrassed she was ready to sink through the floor and she didn't speak to her husband for the rest of the week.

Naturally she was quite upset now at the prospect of a dinner guest.

"Cyrian says to tell you not to go to any trouble," Uncle Stanley reported. "Just put an extra plate on the table."

"Stanley!" she started to protest, but he had already hung up. When she replaced her own receiver, her hand was quite clammy.

She took two aspirins, a Bromo Seltzer and some note paper and tried to make out a menu.

Her hair was a mess. The silver hadn't been polished. There wasn't time to get another order from the butcher so she would have to make meat loaf and somehow or other she must find time to bake a cake.

Ordinarily when she was having dinner guests, she

stayed awake nights for a week planning and replanning the meal, though no matter how carefully she tried to arrange things ahead of time, the whole dinner always seemed to need attention at once so that when she sat down to the table she was hot and disheveled.

Then she kept bobbing up and down for things she had forgotten and passing and repassing the butter and corn relish until no one had time to eat. If her guests refused a second helping, she was mortally certain they weren't enjoying their meal, but if they praised her cooking, her neck flushed and she began to apologize, saying she didn't know what had gone wrong with the oven because nothing had come out right.

Now she turned on the bath water so it could run while she peeled the potatoes and prepared the meat. By the time she slid them in the oven her breath was coming in nervous gasps and she was certain she had forgotten to put salt in the meat loaf but she didn't want to risk adding it now for fear she was wrong.

She put the cake ingredients into the electric mixer bowl and carried the appliance with her to the bathroom. The water in the tub had only overflowed a little. She mopped it up and plugged in the electric mixer, planning to allow it to do its work while she took her bath.

She had just climbed into the tub when she heard the downstairs door open. Her next-door neighbor Ethel Wilcox who always walked in without knocking called, "Anyone home?"

She didn't want Ethel snooping around downstairs so she called "I'll be down in a minute."

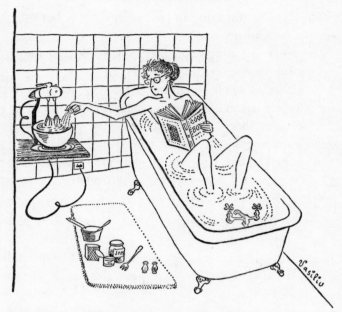

Either accidentally or on purpose Ethel chose to interpret this as an invitation to come upstairs.

When she heard the ascending footsteps Aunt Daphne remembered the bathroom door was unlocked. Ethel **was** perfectly capable of marching right in.

Aunt Daphne had one foot in the tub and the other **on** the bath mat when, in her haste, she accidentally knocked the electric mixer from the shelf into the tub.

There was a loud crackling and the sput of blue flame.

When Uncle Stanley and his guest reached the house, they found it overrun with neighbors, the doctor and the police and fire departments.

Aunt Daphne was lying in bed, pale, shaken, but miraculously alive and unhurt.

"The meat loaf caught on fire," she whispered faintly. "You'll have to open a can of beans."

Uncle Stanley knelt beside her. "Honey," he said, "the chief of police has to make out a report to explain how you got an electric shock. He wants to know why on earth you were mixing a cake in the bathroom."

But Aunt Daphne had had all she could stand for one day. "You just tell him for me," she declared, "that he can mind his own business."

TWENTY-SIX

The Nesting Instinct

While some of Uncle Stanley's inventions were a little odd, like the flat wiener which would stay in place in a bun without rolling out, none of us ventured to say anything around Aunt Daphne.

"Stanley has his little ways," she sometimes said, "but at least *he* doesn't go around climbing trees."

Of course, as Mother admitted later, if she had thought things over carefully, she never would have done it either.

Mother was an ardent bird-lover—not in cages. She could never bear to see even canaries kept prisoner. She belonged to the Audubon Society and anywhere in the house you were apt to find cryptic notes that said, "pied-billed Grebe, Aug. 1st, nr. beach."

Each summer the family had to use the back entrance of the house because a pair of robins with overdeveloped reproductive instincts (sometimes they raised as many as three families in a season) always nested on the front porch.

Father, who could take his birds or leave them alone, was rash enough to suggest that the nest be torn down as soon as it was started so that the pair would become discouraged and build someplace else and he could enjoy his porch in peace.

Mother gave him a reproving stare. "How," she asked, "would you like to be a robin with no place to lay your egg?"

Father said he had never quite thought of it that way before, and took refuge behind his newspaper.

Mother had a profound reverence for birds' nests. They were, she was fond of saying, genuine works of art. Indeed the only time she was ever known to speak harshly to Mrs. Shroeder, our cleaning woman, was when a hummingbird's nest that had been given to her by the iceman was accidentally thrown out.

"It wasn't even as if it was my second-best hummingbird's nest," Mother said indignantly. "I have one that is three years old, but this one was so fresh the lichens were still green."

The occasion when Mother climbed the apple tree was a mistake from beginning to end.

In the first place she wasn't dressed properly. She had planned to attend a meeting of the Women's Institute and she was wearing a blue dressmaker suit, white gloves and a hat bordered with poppies and white field daisies.

In the second place Mother was not exactly constructed on tree-climbing lines. She was what is optimistically referred to in the fashion ads as stylishly stout. She went through life intending to do something about this next week.

On this occasion she was on her way out to the garage when she happened to glance up in the apple tree. What she saw there threw her into a perfect frenzy of excitement.

In the tree was a nest, a nest, moreover, which no matter how she cricked and craned her neck, Mother was unable to identify. It wasn't round and solid enough for a robin's, or basket-enough-like for an oriole's. It might be a catbird's, but she was almost positive that it belonged to a tanager.

It occurred to her that if she got a stepladder and stood on it, she might have a better view. The stepladder proved much too short, but it was high enough for her to climb comfortably on to the solid lower branch of the apple tree.

It was close to twenty-five years since Mother had climbed a tree and it must have gone to her head. She began to climb higher and higher.

She had no trouble getting up, but when she went to go down a new problem arose. She was stuck.

Mother perched on a stout branch next to the trunk, drew on her white gloves (which she had had the foresight to tuck in her pocket) and considered the situation. No one was home. The nearest neighbors were so far away that even if she called for help, no one was apt to hear her.

She spent the entire afternoon up the tree.

Once old Silas Cobby who cared for the neighborhood lawns when he was sober came stumbling by, but he took to his heels when he heard her voice suddenly coming out of the heavens.

Father had stopped by at the school for us, but it was well past four when we finally arrived home. We had hardly gotten out of the car when we heard Mother calling to us in a somewhat perturbed voice.

It was a little while before we located her.

"Flora!" Father cried in a scandalized voice. "Whatever are you doing up that tree! Come down at once!"

"I can't," Mother protested. "I'm stuck."

"You've got your white gloves on," one of my sisters said, in some surprise.

"That has nothing to do with it," Mother answered. "Just find a ladder and get me out of here."

Unfortunately, our only ladder was the short one already leaning against the tree.

Father went about the neighborhood but, though he collected several people willing to offer advice, he couldn't find a long enough ladder.

Eventually he had the brilliant idea of calling the volunteer fire department.

The firemen roared up in a magnificent clamor of red engines and sirens. Father explained the situation. With the utmost efficiency and tact the men raised a ladder. Dr. Cowan, the fire chief, himself, carefully helped Mother down from the tree while the entire neighborhood stood around and applauded.

Mother gave a little sigh of relief as she stood on solid ground again. She straightened the hat with the poppies

and daisies and brushed bits of bark from her little white gloves.

"You gentlemen have been so kind," she said with dignity. "Won't you come in and have a cup of tea? I'm certain I can find a chocolate cake."

"Personally," said Father, "I'm going to need two cups of tea. Whatever possessed you, Flora? You might have broken your neck."

Mother gave him her most angelic smile. "I'm very sorry, Angus," she said. "It was dreadful of me to make so much trouble for everyone. Besides, it wasn't a tanager's nest after all. It belonged to a cedar waxwing."

As far as anyone knows, Mother never climbed a tree again.

·TWENTY-SEVEN·

Jungle Passion

Being helped down out of a tree by the volunteer fire department was a somewhat embarrassing experience, but Mother always said that the worst thing that ever happened to her in her entire life was the dinner party given by the Roger Dickensheets on their twentieth (china) wedding anniversary. It was quite a nice affair, with violets floating in the finger bowls.

Mother loved parties, though Father was something of a problem. It was hard to get him to go in the first place, but once she got him there, it was even harder to get him to go home.

At first the Dickensheets' party seemed very successful. The roast beef was good, Mother had a new dress, trimmed with pearl beads, and Father was obviously having a fine time.

Mother was very proud of Father and sometimes she felt a little sorry for women who weren't married to him.

Mother's dinner partner was a small vegetable of a man with ears like fried potatoes and a head somewhat the shape of an eggplant. He was a mining man, just back

221

from twelve years in Africa, and Mrs. Dickensheet had asked her to be particularly nice to him.

Mother tried to remember his name—it was something to do with money, she was certain. Mother always had trouble remembering names and she tried to associate them with something. Mr. Penny, she thought. It turned out later that his name was actually Nickleson, but by that time it was too late to matter.

Mr. Penny (or Nickleson) was obviously ill at ease. Mother, who never could bear to see anyone uncomfortable, gave him her warmest, sweetest smile.

"Canada must seem strange after being away so long," she said.

He took a quick gulp of water, as if to oil his vocal cords. His voice was a little worn and squeaky like an Edison phonograph cylinder. "I didn't see a white woman for five years," he said.

"Really?" said Mother, and then, in a much sharper tone, "Really!" She must have overdone the friendliness, she thought in amazement, for under the table there was a firm, unmistakable pressure against her knee. Nothing like this had ever happened to her before. It was true of course that she had a cuddly sort of sweetness men seemed to find appealing, but up until now, only in a very respectful way.

Something brushed against her knee again.

Mother could feel her neck beginning to flush. She had never been in such an outrageous situation in her entire life, but she was a gentle woman and she felt she mustn't

judge him too harshly. "Mr. Penny," she said, quite kindly considering the circumstances, "I'm afraid you are making a serious mistake. You seem to have forgotten certain rules of behavior."

Mr. Penny looked down at the silverware, gulped and seemed incapable of speech.

Bits of forgotten misinformation from her high-school days bubbled through Mother's mind. She remembered the sinister things she had heard that the heat and rot of the jungle did to a white man's morals. She thought of the Sabine women and the missionary and Sadie Thompson.

It just proved, Mother thought, that you couldn't tell a person's character by looking at him. Whoever would think that such a shy-looking little man would have such unconventional ideas?

She was about to turn away from him when the pressure on her knee was repeated. This was going altogether too far and something should be done about it.

Mr. Penny stared wildly at her from a face crimsoned by either shame or passion. He must be completely crazy, Mother thought.

She looked about her for help. Father was eating his roast beef with an air of enjoyment. No one seemed even aware of her predicament. Mother didn't want to create a scene and she just didn't know what to do. She considered the tines of her fork as a possible weapon of defense. Then she took a deep breath. She remembered Great-grandma Lawton, who had dealt with a drunken

Indian who broke into her cabin when she was alone, by giving him a stern lecture and making him drink hot maple syrup. (The maple syrup was supposed to sober him up but Father said the very thought of it would put a man off his liquor for life.)

"Mr. Penny," Mother said, her voice sizzling quietly like a Dominion Day firecracker. "You should be ashamed of yourself. I tried to be friendly because you are a stranger. There certainly is no excuse for the way you've behaved. I intend to tell my husband."

Mr. Penny's eyes swam like nervous minnows behind his thick-lensed glasses. From red he turned the color of a sliced Bermuda onion. He opened his lips, but after a few gasps that suggested he needed rewinding, no sound came.

Mother turned haughtily to her other neighbor, Mr. Elgin, who worked in the office at Ford's and collected buttons. Again came the pressure on Mother's leg, but this time from Mr. Elgin's direction. For one terrible moment Mother wondered if the whole world had gone mad. She stared down at her lap. The black nose of Trafalgar, the Dickensheets' spaniel, appeared below the tablecloth, silently coaxing her for food.

Mother wished she could drop right through the floor. Her first impulse was to call attention to the culprit, but on second thought, she changed her mind. While Mr. Penny was no doubt completely bewildered by her outburst, that at least was better than having him know she had credited him with the spaniel's enthusiasm.

Certainly she would never live it down if her friends ever heard the story.

The room had become unbearably hot and Mother sweltered in the steam box of her thoughts. In a life as virtuous as hers, there were so few occasions to use her conscience that now she was deluged with its full strength. She remembered every sin she had committed in her entire life. She recalled a most embarrassing incident her first day in school when she was too shy to ask the location of the washroom. She remembered the time she had picked a rose in a public park and that once, before she was married, she had talked to a strange young man in the ice-cream parlor without being introduced.

Mother had read somewhere that when you are disturbed emotionally, you should think of something pleasant. She thought of her children, chocolate éclairs and lilacs. She went through the alphabet—apples—babies—candy—dogs—

Someone, she thought, should write a book about a party that never seemed to end and then it would turn out that everyone was dead and had gone to the bad place.

She didn't blame Mr. Penny for avoiding her, but later, in the living room, it was apparent that he was afraid of everyone. When spoken to, he flinched.

Mother felt just like crying. She had always had a very vivid imagination. She pictured Mr. Penny in his hammock in the jungle, counting the days, the hours and the minutes until he could be in civilization again. He had come to them, asking only kindness and she had turned on him like a fishwife. How terribly bewildered and hurt he must feel.

Mother couldn't stand it any longer. No matter how it embarrassed her, she would explain so that he would know it was not he who had been at fault.

When the party—with the exception of Father—was beginning to break up, she sought out Mr. Penny.

She knotted her handkerchief, thought of the sun shining on the blue lake water, and began bravely. "Mr. Penny, I'm so ashamed. I don't know what you must think of me."

He began to back nervously towards the hall. "It's quite all right, Mrs. Tippett. It's quite all right. I'm sure things must have changed a great deal since I went away."

Before she could say another word he was down the hall with the speed of a frightened rabbit and out the door without even stopping to speak to his hostess.

Mother looked after him in dismay. Goodness, she thought, he really is a queer little man.

It wasn't until some moments later that she had a very startling thought. She wondered if by any chance Trafalgar had made advances to Mr. Penny.

·TWENTY-EIGHT·

Cousin Edward and the Sea Serpent

The thing about writing about your own family is that the relatives divide into two groups. There are the ones who scamper joyously into closets lugging out all available skeletons, like terriers with a bone, and there are the others who wrap the past in a decent shroud of British reticence and say in genuine horror, "But my dear, you couldn't possibly tell that!"

"I'll change names and places," you promise recklessly. "I'll be very careful."

But in the end it is a compromise. You reach once more into memory's helter-skelter grab bag. "All right," you agree, "I won't tell how the toilet bowl happened to get cracked that time Aunt Lucy visited us if you let me tell about Cousin Edward and the sea serpent."

"Oh that," they sigh in relief. "No one is going to believe it anyhow."

And perhaps they won't.

Our forty-second cousin Edward is the only person I have ever known whose life was influenced by a sea serpent.

Edward was an only son who lived with his widowed mother at Ridgetown in a brown bungalow with a nasturtium bed edged by whitewashed pebbles. Aunt Fern was the sort of woman who goes through life demanding to talk to the manager; but in a sort of way, all of us liked Edward.

For as long as I could remember, Aunt Fern and Edward had spent two weeks with us each summer. None of us looked forward to these visits with much enthusiasm.

In the first place Aunt Fern had ideas about posture and was continually urging Mother to make us wear shoulder braces so we wouldn't grow up to be round-shouldered.

Her own son wore one for years, a weird contraption consisting of yards of straps and buckles. He turned out to be round-shouldered anyhow, so we could only imagine what he might have been without the braces.

Edward was painfully shy even around us girls. If cornered into a conversation he was apt to come up with odd bits of flotsam like Did you know that a cricket's ears are in its knees? However, he liked to talk to Mother, but then all men did.

Mother was quite fond of him too. "Such a nice young man," she often said. "And so good to poor Fern." This was in the days before it was considered a little sinister to be good to your mother.

At the time of his mishap with the sea serpent, Edward was around twenty-three, rather slight, with an odd shuffling walk as if his shoelaces had just come untied. He had a good job in a bank where he wore well-brushed blue suits and acquired a red ridge on his neck from wearing thickly starched shirts.

He was a very considerate visitor, much more so than his mother. In hot weather he sometimes suffered from asthma and rather than disturb the household with his coughing, he would get up and go out on the far end of our dock where he could wheeze in peace and read by the aid of a flashlight.

As a matter of fact, he always felt that it was probably the flashlight that originally attracted the sea serpent's attention.

Around dawn one morning he was finishing a chapter of *Anthony Adverse* when he heard an odd noise close to the dock. (His asthma had cleared, as it usually did towards morning, but he was a slow reader and he never liked to stop in the middle of a chapter.)

Peering through his bifocals, he beheld the most incredible object ever seen in the Detroit River. As he himself described it later, it was a creature some fifteen feet long, a darkish-gray green in color, with a head and neck somewhat resembling pictures he had seen of dinosaurs.

The novel Edward was reading slipped into the river as he jerked back his legs (he was wearing gray felt bedroom slippers) and began a cautious retreat from the dock, not certain but that the creature might have some means of locomotion on shore and attack him. The sea serpent, however, seemed content to mind its own business, though it took a tentative nibble at a floating page of the book.

Edward recovered his equilibrium and ran for the house.

Apparently it occurred to him that he should have some record of this momentous occasion. Forgetting his usual shyness, he burst into our bedroom demanding in a loud, agitated manner, if he could borrow a camera.

It seemed a peculiar request at that time of day but I got mine from the bottom bureau drawer.

The camera was a Brownie box, held together by elastic bands, and was unloaded at the time, a circumstance which I neglected to tell Edward. Later he was very nice about the whole thing, but it was obvious he felt that I alone was responsible for the fact that he couldn't show the world a portrait of the sea serpent calmly munching on the waterlogged pages of *Anthony Adverse*.

By now Edward's shouts had roused the rest of the household, including Aunt Fern, who was fond of declaring she never closed her eyes all night, though actually she snored like a coal-barge foghorn for nine hours straight. Still dazed from sleep and unable to understand Edward's excitement, she couldn't decide if the house was on fire or being burglarized. She picked up the telephone receiver and screamed, "Get the fire department! Get the police!" and hung up, leaving the problem to the operator.

In the meantime Edward had disappeared. We found him crouched in his blue striped pajamas out on the dock, aiming the empty camera at the river.

"Edward!" we cried. "Edward! Whatever is wrong?"

It was this commotion, Edward claimed later, that frightened away the sea serpent. It pricked up its ears. (On later cross-examination he faltered on this point. He wasn't entirely certain it had ears, but it did lift its head in a questioning, intelligent manner.) Then submerging like a submarine, it vanished swiftly from sight.

All this excitement brought on another attack of Edward's asthma. My sister Bonnie, in a misguided attempt to revive him, filled a bait can with rainwater from a rowboat and poured it over his head.

When the volunteer fire department and the police patrol car rushed up and saw Edward gasping feebly on the dock with his hair like seaweed, they naturally concluded that he had just been rescued from the river and proceeded to apply artificial respiration with so much enthusiasm it was a miracle he was ever able to breathe again.

By the time poor Edward recovered sufficient lung power to tell his story, the serpent was completely out of sight.

There was a moment's tactful silence.

"You just get back from an all-night party?" one of the policemen asked.

"My son," Aunt Fern declared haughtily, "does not drink and is not in the habit of going to all-night parties."

"Sea serpent, ha! ha!" snickered one of the volunteer firemen.

"Edward," said our mother, "is a very truthful person. If he says he saw a sea serpent, I am sure he did."

With the party line thus clearly defined, there was no reneging. We were a clannish family and from now on, in public at least, we were definitely committed to Edward and the sea serpent.

Privately, we had our doubts. Edward had not only been groggy from lack of sleep, he was so nearsighted that even after all these years he had trouble telling my sisters and me apart. Frankly, we suspected that in the dim light of early dawn Edward couldn't tell the difference between a submerged log and a sea serpent unless it bit him.

We did, however, feel that he was completely sincere. Never once in the hectic days that followed did he yield to the temptation to embroider his story. He had seen a sea serpent, but it was just a common, ordinary, everyday sea serpent. It didn't breathe fire or increase in size, and while *Anthony Adverse* might be considered a surprising item of diet, it had undoubtedly been hungry.

The story was carried by the Associated Press accompanied by a picture of Edward standing on the dock with his right index finger pointing in the direction of the river to indicate he went thataway.

Our dock swarmed with total strangers, nibbling on bananas and seeking the sea serpent. Some were skeptical at the top of their lungs. Others had the unmitigated gall to pretend that they too could see the serpent, a frank piece of encroachment, since the creature was obviously Edward's private property.

We were so mortified about the whole business it took a little while to realize that for the first time in family history, Edward was a social asset.

By now all our friends were convinced that the entire affair was a practical joke. "Do bring your cousin with the wonderful sense of humor," they said.

Edward, who up until now had never been anything but a hopeless dud at a party, was first astounded, then accepted as his just due the fact that his most ordinary remarks were greeted with admiring laughter. He began taking our prettiest girl friends out onto the porch swing and telling them the facts of life, like Did you know a housefly has sticky pads on its feet which help it to walk upside down on ceilings?

As a matter of fact we ourselves were never quite certain whether he was being funny or whether he was just being Edward.

Aunt Fern protested indignantly against her son's man-about-town life, but Edward said politely he might as well stay awake at parties as stay awake with asthma. Oddly enough, however, he never had another asthmatic attack.

Edward's vacation came to a reluctant conclusion. We walked out to the dock for a farewell look, but the serpent was not in sight.

He kissed all of us good-bye (now he even knew us apart).

"This has been a very interesting experience," he said earnestly. "But I've learned a lesson. Next time I see a sea serpent, I'm going to keep it to myself."

·TWENTY-NINE·

The Galloping Subconscious

Even before he had all that trouble with the sea serpent, Cousin Edward was a hard man to get up in the morning. You could shake him, yell or even sprinkle him with cold water, but he would only grunt and roll over.

During the year he stayed with us, the family finally rebelled at this morning chore (after all, we had enough trouble waking up ourselves). Edward bought six alarm clocks, set them at two-minute intervals and hid them in various parts of his bedroom.

He reasoned that he would have to open up a bureau drawer, take out a clock, turn it off and then before he had time to climb back in bed, another alarm would go off. He was optimistic enough to feel that after he had turned off six clocks he would be ready to start the day.

Of course it didn't work out that way at all.

At six-thirty the first alarm blared off. Edward snored on even when the second and third alarms joined in an anvil chorus. If the alarms didn't waken Edward, at least they succeeded in rousing the rest of the household. While he continued to slumber, we scrambled drowsily and grouchily about the room, peering behind the stamp albums on the closet shelves, poking under the bed and behind the golden-oak bureau, trying to locate those infernal, clamoring alarms.

The only thing that ever really aroused Edward was the smell of coffee. If you took a fresh pot and held it close under his king-size nose, he would begin to open one eye. The trick then was to hand him a strong hot black cupful before he went back to sleep. By the time he had been refueled with at least three cups, he would shake himself like a Model T on a cold morning and yawn his way into the unfriendly world.

It wasn't that Edward was lazy. He was just plain tuckered out. He was a sleepwalker, or to put it more accurately, a sleeprunner.

Around two or so in the morning we would be aroused by a thud and then the sound of footsteps furiously pounding along the second-floor corridor, down the back stairs that led into the kitchen, across the kitchen into the lower hall, and then up the front stairs into the second-floor corridor again, back down the rear stairs, and on and on.

Edward would repeat the entire process several times until at last, somewhat out of breath, he would return to his own room and crawl cozily under the covers.

Next morning he would have absolutely no remembrance of his escapade and indeed was apt to be somewhat indignant and skeptical when told. The only thing that actually convinced him was the grime on the bottom of his feet. He was always scrupulous about taking a bath before he went to bed, but next morning his soles were always dirty.

No one was ever able to catch up with him on one of these flights—if clocked he would undoubtedly have broken a world record.

We were careful never to try to waken him, since we had been told the shock might be dangerous, but sometimes we stood to one side and watched in the faint glow of the night light as he came charging by with rumpled hair and flying pajama tails.

He not only was fast, he must have had a radar sense like a bat. Even in the dark he never tripped and if there was an object in his path he would swerve skilfully around it.

This went on for some months and it got so no one paid any attention to him. We would hear that familiar thud in the night, then the swift beat of flat feet, and think, "There's Edward at it again" and go back to sleep.

Only rarely did he vary his routine. One hot August night he thrust his bristling head out the front window and bellowed "Help! Police! Help!" for about five minutes. This roused our neighbors, but not the police department. They must have been deaf.

Around this time Edward's sleeprunning began to take a new form. He not only ran up and down the stairs, he ran along the narrow ornamental iron rod that formed the head of his bed. It was a feat which might have given a cat trouble, but Edward performed it with the greatest of ease, staring glassily ahead and swinging on his toes.

Vasiliu.

The odd part was that Edward had never at any time been even remotely an athlete. He was rather frail, with thin hair and bifocals and when he was awake, he would undoubtedly have had trouble outrunning an elderly arthritic lady.

Mother seemed to find his antics on the bedrail a trifle disturbing.

"I don't mind people sleepwalking," she declared, "but this is going altogether too far."

Indeed it was a little unnerving to see him scurry along his precarious foothold, pivot on one foot on the brass knob and then race back.

She gave him an ultimatum. It was simply impossible to keep the sheets clean, she said. If Edward intended to keep on walking in his sleep, the least he could do was put his bedroom slippers on first. (I think she had a cunning hope that the leather soles would prevent him from balancing on the bed.)

Edward seemed to feel that this request was only reasonable and promised to try to remember, but next morning there were the clean sheets embroidered with grubby toeprints.

The only thing to do, Mother decided, was cure Edward of sleepwalking.

This was easier said than done.

For a time Edward fell asleep every night murmuring over and over, "I will not walk in my sleep tonight—I will not walk—I will not—will not—"

But he did.

In desperation he turned his room into an obstacle course tying a rope firmly across the door and scattering tacks on the floor. That night he balanced on the rope and pranced across the tacks with all the aplomb of a Hindu fakir.

When he woke up in the morning there were a couple of tacks dotted in his calluses like cloves in ham. It's a mercy he didn't get blood poisoning.

We had just about given him up as hopeless when Mother discovered psychiatry.

She came home from a meeting of the Daughters of the Empire all atwitter. "Did you ever hear of Freud?" she asked Edward.

Edward looked a little doubtful. "There used to be a family on the next street, but I think their name was Freeman."

"He was a doctor who wrote books about why people do what they do," she explained. "Do you know what makes you run in your sleep?"

"If I did," Edward answered simply, "I wouldn't do it."

"That's it entirely," Mother cried in triumph. "It's your subconscious mind. You've a suppressed desire. That's what makes you have nightmares."

Edward wore the baffled look of a man who thinks he may have been insulted, but isn't entirely sure.

Mother presented him with a book. "I got this for you at the library. As our speaker explained today, you must learn to face the reality of the real you."

"Applesauce," mumbled Edward, but he took the book

obediently enough and began to read.

As he read his neck grew redder and redder. "Well, I never!" he gulped in a shocked voice, "Flora, have you read this book?"

"I haven't had time," Mother admitted.

"I should think not!" roared Edward. "And what's more, it isn't fit to be in the same house as young, innocent girls. It's going right back to the library, and I'll insist that they keep it on the locked shelves."

He snatched the book up under his arm. "You," he snorted, glaring at Mother, "should be ashamed of yourself! I've often wondered what women talk about at club meetings. Now I know."

"Goodness," said Mother, staring after him. "I wonder what *is* wrong with his subconscious. I always thought Edward was such a nice boy."

Edward came back from the library still so miffed he didn't even stop for his regular bedtime snack of Welsh rarebit on toast.

That night for the first night in months Edward didn't run up and down in his sleep.

Mother was quite delighted. "No matter what Edward says, we can just thank Dr. Freud," she said. "Unless of course it was the Welsh rarebit."

I've told about Mother's law-breaking activities and Father's garden in the bathtub and Uncle Stanley's strange inventions and Cousin Edward's sea serpent. I've told so many things it does seem rather a shame not to tell about the dreadful mishap that befell poor Aunt Lucy in our bathroom.

But some things are sacred.

july 1970